THE UNIVERSITY OF CHICAGO

Perception of the Drought Hazard on the Great Plains

DEPARTMENT OF GEOGRAPHY
RESEARCH PAPER NO. 106

By

Thomas Frederick Saarinen

The University of Arizona

CHICAGO · ILLINOIS
1966

Library of Congress Catalog Card Number: 66-22754

ACKNOWLEDGMENTS

From the first proposal through the periods of field work, and
analysis, to the time of final publication the author has been aided by
the advice, encouragement, and information provided by many persons and
institutions. It is difficult, even impossible, to single out all who
contributed in these various ways but at least some of the major debts
can be acknowledged.

The author owes an intellectual debt to the staff and students
of the Department of Geography of the University of Chicago. In the stimu-
lating atmosphere provided by them and by other portions of the University
the original proposal was made, the analysis completed, and the first draft
written.

The study was made under a fellowship granted by Resources for the
Future, Inc., but the conclusions, opinions, and other statements contained
herein are those of the writer and are not necessarily those of the Resources for the Future, Inc.

During a preliminary period of reconnaissance work in the Great
Plains, scores of farmers, local, state and federal officials, and university
personnel gave generously of their time, advice and impressions. At this
and earlier stages important sets of data were provided by the Federal Crop
Insurance Corporation and The Agricultural Stabilization and Conservation
Service.

Individuals who were particularly helpful during some of the earlier
stages were John W. Bennett, Leslie Hewes and Arlen Lutz who suggested certain questions, Wayne C. Palmer who provided detailed information on past
drought periods, and William E. Henry who encouraged the use and helped in
the selection of suitable TAT cards.

During the period of field work many local ASC and SCS officials
provided help. The author is especially grateful to the 96 farmers who
served as subjects and the six following county agents who provided letters
of introduction to them as well as other essential information: Howard
Temple of Adams County, Raymond G. Sall of Frontier County, Bruce G. Whitmore

of Kiowa County, Kenneth Fromm of Finney County, Ferrell Smith of Cimarron County and Ray Etheridge of Barber County.

The final manuscript benefited greatly by the comments, corrections and questions raised by those who read all or portions of a review draft. The following, generously, performed this task; Alan M. Baker, Robert Beck, John W. Bennett, Brian J. L. Berry, Wesley C. Calef, Andrew B. Erhart, Ray Etheridge, Robert H. Fuller, Norton W. Ginsberg, R. L. Heathcote, Melvin E. Hecht, Leslie Hewes, Ella M. Irwin, Robert W. Kates, Robert C. Lucas, Arlen Lutz, Marvin W. Mikesell, Robert A. Murdie, Wayne C. Palmer, Kerry J. Pataki, Philip W. Porter, Frank J. Quinn, Raymond G. Sall, W. R. Derrick Sewell, John Sims, Albert E. Smith, Ferrell Smith, Joseph Sonnenfeld, Don Stearley, Howard Temple, Gilbert F. White, Bruce G. Whitmore and Shue Tuck Wong. Their efforts are appreciated and individually they may recognize some of the revisions which have resulted.

The maps were made by Mrs. Sue Weller. The final manuscript was typed by Mrs. Marie P. Fitzmaurice who did much to put it into proper form.

The psychological interpretations of the TAT stories owe much to the special skills of John Sims with whom the author worked in learning the group interpretation method.

But from beginning to end, the most important source of guidance was Gilbert F. White who provided not only good advice, but something far rarer, a good example.

TABLE OF CONTENTS

LIST OF TABLES

LIST OF ILLUSTRATIONS

CHAPTER I

DROUGHT AND THE GREAT PLAINS

Well I'd say this was a scene in Western Kansas in the dirty 30s. Because of the great opportunities in the late 20s and early 30s this farmer moved to the drylands of the High Plains. His first few years were very successful in harvesting good crops and increasing his bank account. Each year more land was plowed up, vegetation destroyed and lack of moisture made a situation perfect for wind erosion. And for the next four or five years the wind blew and the soil drifted and the farmer's bank account and assets were liquidated. And in despair with his hands in his pockets, and his head bent low he started his return to the big city.[1]

Introduction

Failure to accurately perceive the drought hazard[2] has been the focal problem on the Great Plains since farmers from humid areas first settled there in the late nineteenth century. A large part of this problem stems from the basic uncertainty of weather conditions in the area.[3] Even if the market

---

[1] This story and all others at the start of each chapter were among those told by Great Plains wheat farmers in response to pictures presented as part of the data-gathering process. For the underlying rationale see chapter iii and for interpretation of some of the stories see chapter vii.

[2] Hazard as used here includes both risk and uncertainty. The former is used to describe outcomes with a known probability distribution; the latter, outcomes which are uncertain. This distinction will be retained throughout the remainder of the discussion.

[3] Perhaps the best discussion of the uncertainty of weather conditions in the area is contained in C. Warren Thornthwaite, "The Great Plains," Migration and Economic Opportunity, the Report of the Study of Population Redistribution, ed. Carter Goodrich, Bushrod W. Allin, C. Warren Thornthwaite and others (Philadelphia: University of Pennsylvania Press, 1936), pp. 202-250.

conditions were stabilized there would still be great differences in crop and pasture yields from year to year due to the wide variation in rainfall from season to season. Studies of tree rings, lake levels, or the longest available climatic records have failed to reveal any cyclical recurrence to the drought conditions.[1] And since much of the rainfall results from relatively small localized showers, there may be wide variations in amount within short distances in any single year. Truly, here are conditions of great risk and dramatic uncertainty. The resource manager[2] may know that there is a good probability of drought over the long run but when exactly the next one will occur is uncertain.

There has been much discussion of the means by which a more favorable adjustment to this semiarid area might take place. Many investigators have tried to work out the most stable kind of crop combinations, the optimal farm size, and the most effective types of institutional arrangements.[3] But very

---

[1]For a thorough discussion of various attempts to find regularities in the recurrence of droughts, see Ivan R. Tannehill, Drought; Its Causes and Effects (Princeton, N.J.: Princeton University Press, 1947). See also his later article, Ivan R. Tannehill, "Is Weather Subject To Cycles?" Water, 1955 Yearbook of Agriculture (Washington: U. S. Government Printing Office, 1955), pp. 84-90. A series of maps depicting areas of drought in Western North America since 1500 fails to reveal any simple recurring cycle. The maps were based on tree ring information compiled by the Laboratory of Tree-Ring Research of the University of Arizona. See Harold C. Fritts, "Tree-Ring Evidence for Climatic Changes in Western North America," Monthly Weather Review, XCIII, No. 7 (1965), 421-442.

[2]Resource manager as used in this paper refers only to the farmers and ranchers of the Great Plains.

[3]For a general overview of farm size and land use, adjustments, see Agriculture Research Service, "Farming in the Great Plains, A Survey of the Financial and Tenure Situation in 1957," United States Department of Agriculture Production Research Report No. 50 (Washington: U. S. Government Printing Office, 1961). Examples of studies focussing more directly on certain areas are those on various parts of Montana by L. C. Rude, "Land Use Alternatives for Dryland Grain-Livestock Operators," Montana Agricultural Experiment Station Bulletins 570, 571 and 572 (Bozeman, 1962); or the series by Ronald D. Krenz and Thomas A. Miller, "Wheat Farming in Wyoming," University of Wyoming Agricultural Experiment Station Bulletins 391, 392 and 397 (Laramie, 1962). An approach which develops models to estimate variability arising from alternative farming and ranching systems is that exemplified by Wallace A. Aanderud, "Income Variability of Alternative Plans, Selected Farm and Ranch Situations, Rolling Plains of Northwest Oklahoma" (unpublished Ph.D. dissertation, Dept. of Agricultural Economics, Oklahoma State University, 1964); and Roger H. Willsie, "The Economics of Classifying Farmland between Alternative Uses," Nebraska Agricultural Experiment Station Research Bulletin 208 (Lincoln, 1963). Some examples of studies concerned with institutional arrangements are Frank Alexander and Carl F. Kraenzel, "Rural Social Organization of Sweet Grass County Montana," Montana State College Agricultural Experiment Station Bulletin 490 (Bozeman, 1953); Carl F. Kraenzel, "The Rural Community and the Agricultural Program," Montana Agricultural Experiment Station Bulletin 552 (Bozeman, 1960); or the symposium on the Great Plains with the main emphasis

little attention has been paid to the way in which the central character in the adaptation process views the central problem with which he is faced.[1] The present study focuses on this deficiency. It represents an effort to broadly explore the ways in which the main actor, the Great Plains wheat farmer, perceives his major problem, the drought hazard, and to what extent this perception affects his adaptation to the physical environment. In this study the terms adaptation and adjustment are used interchangeably. Both refer to any changes in personality, society or culture which aid in the maintenance or functioning of a system, or to the achievement of a purpose. Here the purpose is a more harmonious relationship between man and the Great Plains environment. Technology refers to the body of knowledge and skill which is potentially available for technical improvements and inventions. Adaptation and adjustment imply the process of changing or the results of the changes whereas technology may or may not be adopted though potentially available. It is recognized that other factors, such as economic efficiency, are also important in the farmer's decisions. But here they are only mentioned incidentally and the main focus remains the role of perception of the drought hazard by Great Plains farmers.

Hypotheses

In an effort to deepen understanding of how Great Plains wheat farmers perceive the drought hazard several relationships suggested by previous writings about the area are formulated as hypotheses and set up for testing. It is hypothesized that the resource manager's perception of the drought hazard will play a significant role in his decision as to which practices are adopted. Certain sociological studies suggest that sutland-yonland[2] differences will be important factors associated with the degree to which various practices have been adopted. It is further hypothesized that perception of the drought hazard will vary according to (1) the aridity of the area, (2) the amount

---

on institutional adaptations to the environment in *Journal of Farm Economics*, Vol. XXXII, No. 3 (1950).

[1]Another writer recently called attention to the same deficiency saying "we have a reasonable amount of information about farming and the rural landscape, but . . . we know very little about farmers." W. M. Williams, "The Social Study of Family Farming," *Geographical Journal*, CXXIX (1963), 63-74.

[2]These terms were coined by Carl F. Kraenzel; sutland referring to the densely settled areas along transportation lines; yonland, to the more sparsely settled areas beyond. See Carl F. Kraenzel, *The Great Plains in Transition* (Norman: University of Oklahoma Press, 1955), chap. xv. For an attempt to apply these concepts in a Great Plains setting see Courtney B. Cleland, "Sutland and Yonland in North Dakota," *North Dakota Institute for Regional Studies Social Science Report* No. 1 (Fargo: North Dakota Agricultural College, 1955).

and frequency of drought experienced by the manager, and (3) personality differences.

From Area to Personality

The starting point is the area, The Great Plains. This is discussed in chapter i. The main emphasis is on past perceptions of the drought hazard and on the kinds of adaptations farmers have made in dealing with it. This is preceded by a brief discussion of drought and its relative importance in Great Plains wheat farming and a rapid survey of the kinds of adaptations which have been made in the past in other parts of the world with similar climatic conditions. A short concluding section is concerned with the types of personality characteristics usually attributed to Great Plainsmen. Chapter ii examines recent work in the field of perception, particularly that most pertinent for gaining some understanding of man's perception of the natural environment and of natural resources, and the way this affects their use by man. The study plan, choice of areas, type of data gathered, and sampling methods are described in chapter iii. Chapter iv contains evidence gathered for this study related to perception of the drought hazard. Here the perception of the farmers is compared with an objective standard of meteorological drought, the Palmer drought index. Hypotheses are tested using interview data. Chapter v includes discussion of the range of choice as seen by the farmers both in terms of land use and in applicable practices. The degree to which various practices and strategies have been adopted in the different areas is discussed in chapter vi and possible reasons for the differential adoption are considered. In chapter vii the findings related to certain personality characteristics of Great Plains farmers are presented along with the relationship between these and perception and adoption. The major findings of the study are summarized in chapter viii and some suggested implications for public policy and future research are outlined.

The Magnitude of the Problem

Drought is the largest single cause of all insured crop losses in the United States.[1] Of all indemnities paid by the Federal Crop Insurance Corporation drought has accounted for 39 per cent, with the combination of too little

---

[1]The Federal Crop Insurance Corporation has paid indemnities due to more than 120 different specific causes of loss. See Annual Report 1963 Federal Crop Insurance Corporation (Washington: U. S. Department of Agriculture, April, 1964), p. 8.

or too much moisture responsible for over half of the losses. Table 1 shows
that the proportion of losses due to drought is almost three times as great
as the next greatest cause.

TABLE 1

CAUSES OF FCIC LOSSES 1948-1962[a]

Cause	% of All Losses
Drought	39.1
Excess moisture	14.0
Insects	10.9
Hail	10.2
Freeze	10.0
Wind	5.6
Disease	4.8

[a]Taken from Annual Report 1963 Federal
Crop Insurance Corporation.

Wheat is the crop with the largest amount of insurance protection.[1]
Of all wheat crop losses 44.4 per cent were due to drought (see Table 2).
Along with wind it accounted for over half of all wheat crop losses in the
United States during the period 1947-1962, and in two-thirds of these years
it was the largest single cause. The major portion of these drought and wind
losses occurred in the Great Plains. The total for the Central Great Plains
states was over half of the total losses due to drought, and over 70 per cent
of the wheat losses due to wind (see Table 3). Without much fear of error
one could assume that the major portion of these losses was in the Plains
portions of these states.

There are several serious weaknesses in the above data though it is
the most inclusive available. The per cent of the liability insurance in individual counties may range from 5 to 75 per cent.[2] Many counties are not
covered by federal crop insurance since the sharp cut-back in funds to the
Federal Crop Insurance Corporation in 1948. At that time, due to the fact
that indemnities had exceeded premiums during the first seven years of the
program, the scope was reduced to a more limited experimental basis. The

[1]Ibid., p. 24.

[2]These figures are based on statistical material from the files of
the Federal Crop Insurance Corporation.

TABLE 2

CAUSES OF DAMAGE TO WHEAT IN THE UNITED STATES 1947-1962[a]

Year	Drought Bu.	Hail Bu.	Excess Moisture Bu.	Frost,Cold, Freeze, & Winterkill Bu.	Flood Bu.	Wind Bu.	Insects & Pole Burn Bu.	Disease Bu.	All Others Bu.
1947	20,019,362	4,254,597	2,762,643	9,607,323	1,538,671	2,501,151	4,831,858	1,079,952	1,565,544
1948	1,636,881	164,118	25,230	2,075	35,522	12,241	25,186	38,799	85,506
1949	3,550,897	544,776	223,753	607,643	25,040	172,625	182,608	132,330	173,658
1950	513,953	438,878	103,497	206,833	7,668	72,603	311,355	69,589	53,266
1951	1,630,476	938,707	321,055	1,394,453	63,281	55,299	324,854	67,691	122,550
1952	1,753,395	1,046,404	38,851	194,874	18,077	78,181	36,521	127,759	56,397
1953	2,442,794	918,722	211,249	117,056	11,641	264,310	40,359	2,637,341	152,974
1954	1,208,263	886,528	134,934	117,220	25,356	1,100,796	51,250	2,959,275	122,945
1955	3,498,206	655,276	63,083	406,296	1,447	1,362,144	55,749	26,393	248,722
1956	4,079,361	813,097	45,347	133,792	4,376	1,076,750	159,972	10,895	159,055
1957	1,168,329	530,406	335,975	53,858	20,187	466,753	15,964	21,925	69,275
1958	270,173	370,039	54,741	16,689	4,399	32,566	16,033	8,840	14,532
1959	1,268,831	567,781	77,507	177,155	3,785	463,206	76,902	37,834	256,749
1960	284,206	327,563	21,168	215,240	11,232	34,410	5,784	3,996	14,843
1961	2,985,158	525,334	18,239	74,602	28,652	37,013	165,255	71,157	644,275
1962	423,444	519,987	158,001	119,944	4,097	17,820	14,788	119,772	9,044
Total	46,733,729	13,502,213	4,595,273	13,445,053	1,803,431	7,747,868	6,314,438	7,413,548	3,749,335
%	44.4	12.8	4.4	12.8	1.7	7.4	6.0	7.0	3.6

[a]Source County Analysis Sheet, Federal Crop Insurance Corporation.

TABLE 3

CAUSES OF DAMAGE TO WHEAT 1947-1962 BY STATES[a]

(in bushels)

	No. of Counties	Drought	Hail	Excess Moisture	Frost,Cold Freeze & Winterkill	Flood	Wind	Insects & Pole Burn	Diseases	All Others	Total
Nebraska	36	3,821,021	2,424,518	186,398	4,050,165	115,272	770,045	438,259	518,796	255,839	12,580,313
% of State Total		30.4	19.3	1.5	32.2	.9	6.1	3.5	4.1	2.0	
Kansas	100	11,893,832	2,041,674	732,060	2,816,776	244,444	2,591,029	1,137,597	364,306	542,840	22,369,558
% of State Total		53.2	9.1	3.3	12.6	1.1	11.6	5.1	1.6	2.4	
Oklahoma	34	3,818,909	716,851	758,833	640,648	84,358	433,921	1,228,097	254,793	403,171	8,339,581
% of State Total		45.8	8.6	9.1	7.7	1.0	5.2	14.7	3.1	4.8	
Colorado	14	2,749,223	1,122,227	5,359	198,432	2,130	1,771,194	81,592	51,062	152,091	6,133,310
% of State Total		44.8	18.3	.09	3.2	.03	28.9	1.3	.8	2.5	
Total Central Gt.Pl.States	164	22,282,985	6,305,270	1,682,650	7,706,021	451,204	5,566,189	2,885,545	1,188,957	1,353,941	49,422,762
% Cent.Gt.Pl. Total (All Cases)		45.0	12.7	3.4	15.6	.9	11.2	5.8	2.4	2.7	100
% U.S.Total (For cause listed)		47.7	46.7	36.6	57.3	25.0	71.8	45.7	16.0	36.0	46.9

[a]Source County Analysis Sheet, Federal Crop Insurance Corporation, Washington, D.C.

number of counties covered was reduced from 2,500 to 375.[1] Since that time there has been a continual increase in the number of counties covered, so that by 1963, 1,096 were included.[2] At the present time the Federal Crop Insurance Corporation is allowed to increase by 100 counties each year.[3] It is evident that the drought totals alone include a varying number of counties from year to year. Furthermore, many of the areas not covered are the very areas with the greatest risk of drought losses. Following the 1955 crop year the program was withdrawn from fourteen counties in the "Dust Bowl" area after the Corporation had carried the majority of these farmers through the immediately preceding period of extreme drought years.[4] The conclusion is that even these figures, which place drought losses as 44.4 per cent of the total wheat crop losses, tend to underestimate the seriousness of the drought problem in the Great Plains.[5]

While drought clearly is a serious problem for both the Great Plains and the nation as a whole, its precise nature and the human views of drought and adaptation to it are not well understood.

What Is Drought?

Drought differs from other types of natural hazards in terms of its variable duration and areal extent, and the indefiniteness of its beginning and end. Often it is easier to define precisely by its effects after the occurrence than during the period in which it is gradually, imperceptibly becoming more and more severe. One problem is the relative nature of the term drought. It is used to describe a wide range of different conditions.[6] Some

---

[1] William H. Rowe, _Federal Crop Insurance: A Description_ PA-408 (Washington: Federal Crop Insurance Corporation, October, 1959), p. 36.

[2] _Annual Report 1963, Federal Crop Insurance Corporation_, p. 12.

[3] Letter from Mr. John N. Luft, Manager, Federal Crop Insurance Corporation, Washington, D.C., July 31, 1964.

[4] The fourteen counties in the Southwest from which Federal Crop Insurance was withdrawn beginning with the 1956 crop year were Baca, Conejos, Kiowa, Las Animas, Otero and Prowers in Colorado; Childress, Deaf Smith, Hansford, Ochiltree, Runnels and Taylor in Texas; and Curry and Quay in New Mexico. Letter from Mr. John N. Luft, Manager, Federal Crop Insurance Corporation, Washington, D.C., August 13, 1965.

[5] During the period 1948-1963 the Federal Crop Insurance Corporation paid losses of 144.5 million dollars on wheat. See _Annual Report 1963_, p. 26.

[6] The terms used here are those found in C. W. Thornthwait, "Drought," _Encyclopedia Britannica_, VII (1963), 699-701. The concept of yield-reducing invisible drought has often been used to advance the idea of supplemental

of these are: <u>permanent drought</u> where the precipitation is never sufficient to meet the needs as expressed by the potential evapotranspiration; <u>contingent drought</u>, due to variations in precipitation from year to year; seasonal drought, due to an inadequate amount of precipitation in one season though other seasons may be adequate or even excessive in moisture amounts; and <u>invisible drought</u>, which is the case of a borderline inadequacy of rainfall, not quite enough to satisfy the crop needs from month to month, and which shows up only in reduced yields at the end of the year. Thus the drought problem has very different meanings depending on the context.

Each person may be expected to have a different conception of drought depending on his location, his vital interests, and the effect of drought on these interests. An agriculturalist might very quickly come to the conclusion that a drought had begun as he saw the effects of a moisture deficiency during critical periods of plant growth. A meteorologist would soon be aware of any large deviations from normal precipitation patterns. An hydrologist would more likely become concerned about drought when stream flows or lake and reservoir levels fell below normal. The suburban dweller might only become aware of it when water shortages cut down on his lawn sprinkling activities. And the economist would no doubt document drought by reference to the economic effects (see Appendix I for a glossary of drought definitions).

In each of these cases there would be a certain amount of overlap and agreement as to whether there was a drought or not. All would agree, as most definitions do, that drought involved a period of moisture deficiency. But there would be much disagreement as to the amount of moisture deficiency and duration necessary to define drought. The following examples illustrate the great gulf between high and low extremes of the amount and duration of moisture deficiencies considered necessary to define drought. The first from European Russia defines drought as "a period of ten days with a total rainfall not exceeding a fifth of an inch."[1] The second defined by a man interested in very long term trends is "any period in which tree growth was reduced for five or more years has been considered to be a drought period."[2]

---

irrigation in humid areas to overcome seasonal moisture deficiencies not readily perceived by farmers or at least not usually compensated for. A recent example is by John Mather, "The Role of Irrigation Agriculture in Humid Areas." Paper presented at the 61st Annual Meeting of the Association of American Geographers, Columbus, Ohio, April 18-21, 1965. See abstract in <u>Annals AAG</u>, LV, No. 4 (1965), 631.

[1]Taken from discussion of drought definitions by Tannehill, <u>Drought; Its Causes and Effects</u>, p. 37.

[2]Harry E. Weakly, "Recurrence of Drought in the Great Plains During the Last 700 Years, contribution from the Northern Plains Branch, Soil and

Tannehill who wrote what is perhaps the only book on the topic came to the
conclusion that it is useless to try to give a precise definition of drought.[1]

When any of the different views of drought are examined more closely
the difficulties of definition multiply. Agricultural drought has been defined as "a condition of rainfall deficiency with respect to crop production."[2]
But it cannot simply be defined in terms of inches of precipitation because
this would fail to bring out crucial differences in the type of shower,
whether a cloud burst or a gentle soaking rain; or in the timeliness of the
precipitation in terms of stage of growth of the crop; or in the spatial
variations within any small area due to the paths of particular storms.[3]
The more meaningful the definition for a particular purpose the more restricted it must be in terms of specific crops, areas, and level of technology. A recent example is the concept of moisture stress days as applied
to the Ames, Iowa area for corn yields.[4] Here Dale compared the moisture
stress days, as determined by soil moisture supply in the corn root zone and
potential evapotranspiration, with actual corn yields and on this basis could
explain a large amount of the variations in corn yields. However, since the
root zone would vary for different crops and the potential evapotranspiration
would vary at different places, the same sort of computations would have to
be worked out not only for each area being considered but for each crop within
any one area. This somewhat limits the use of the concept for broader comparative purposes.

This difficulty in defining drought is one shared with climatologists
when they try to define the boundaries of the arid climatic zones.[5] The

---

Water Conservation Research Division, Agricultural Research Service, USDA,
in cooperation with Nebraska Agricultural Experiment Station, Lincoln,
Nebraska. (Mimeographed.)

[1]Tannehill, Drought; Its Causes and Effects, p. 39.

[2]G. L. Barger, "A Method for Characterizing Drought Intensity in
Iowa," Agronomy Journal, XLI (1949), 13-19.

[3]An interesting study showing the local variations in rainfall resulting from rainstorms is that of C. W. Thornthwaite, "The Life History of Rainstorms: Progress from the Oklahoma Climatic Research Center," Geographical
Review, XXVII (1937), 92-111.

[4]Robert F. Dale, "Changes in Moisture Stress Days Since 1933,"
Weather and Our Food Supply, CAED Report 20 (Ames, Iowa: Center for Agricultural and Economic Development, 1964), pp. 23-43.

[5]For discussions of these difficulties, see F. K. Hare, "Climatic
Classification, London Essays in Geography, ed. L. D. Stamp and S. W.
Woolridge (Cambridge: Harvard University Press, 1951), chap. vii; and
C. Warren Thornthwaite, "Problems in the Classification of Climates," Geo-
graphical Review, XXXIII, No. 2 (1943), 233-255.

Köppen system marked a great advance when it tried to reduce the climatic complexities to a simple numerically based system which reflected the broad regional differences in vegetation. But when Russell applied Köppen's aridity criteria to the arid western United States he found that the system fit poorly on the boundaries between humid and arid climates and between steppe and desert. Russell showed how the average figures fail to reveal the true picture by introducing his concept of "climatic years" which showed how in different years the boundaries move back and forth in broad transition zones.[1] He drew attention to the importance of the occasional extreme drought in limiting development of plant cover. This whole question of the seeming expansion and contraction of the desert areas is tied in with the intermittent recurrence of drought and Tannehill states, "We must look for the causes in the great elemental forces of the sun, atmosphere, continents, and oceans."[2]

Thornthwaite's climatic classification provided a more sensitive index of differences in arid regions than previous systems.[3] Based on the idea of climatic efficiency, or the capacity of the climates to support the growth of plant communities, it measures this capacity by reference to the annual march of precipitation and temperature and the degree of correlation between these regimes. His moisture index is an indication of the degree to which the water exceeds or is deficient in terms of the available rainfall.[4] Although his method for calculating potential evapotranspiration, the theoretical upper limit of water need, has been subject to some criticism,[5] the Thornthwaite

---

[1]R. J. Russell, "Dry Climates of the United States, II, Frequency of Dry and Desert Years, 1901-1920," University of California (Berkeley) Publications in Geography, V, No. 5 (Berkeley: University of California Press, 1932), 245-274.

[2]Tannehill, Drought; Its Causes and Effects, p. 22.

[3]C. W. Thornthwaite, "An Approach Toward A Rational Classification of Climate," Geographical Review, XXXVII (1948), 55-94.

[4]In this system the moisture index = $\frac{\text{Surplus} - .6 \text{ deficiency}}{\text{need}}$. The moisture index is positive for moist climates, negative for dry climates. The values for various gradations are as follows, -40 - -60 arid, -20 - -40 semiarid, 0 - -20 dry subhumid, 0-20 moist subhumid, 20-100 humid, over 100, perhumid. Instructions for calculating the Thornthwaite moisture index are found in C. W. Thornthwaite and J. R. Mather, "Instructions for Computing Potential Evapotranspiration and the Water Balance," Publications in Climatology, X, No 3 (1957), 181-311.

[5]For example, H. L. Penman, Vegetation and Hydrology, Technical Communication No. 53 Commonwealth Bureau of Soils Harpenden (Farnham Royal, Buckinghamshire, England: Commonwealth Agricultural Bureaux, 1963), 124 pp. See also, William D. Sellers, "Potential Evapotranspiration in Arid Regions," Journal of Applied Meteorology, III (1964), 96-104.

moisture index is generally conceded to be one of the better readily obtainable measures of different degrees of aridity.

A drought index which promises larger usefulness for broad comparative purposes is that recently developed by Palmer of the United States
Weather Bureau. By means of this index one can compare the duration and
severity of droughts widely separated both in time and space. The rationale
for this index of meteorological drought is that,

> the amount of precipitation required for near-normal operation of the
> established economy of an area during some stated period is dependent
> on the average climate of the area and on the prevailing meteorological
> conditions both during and preceding the month or period in question.[1]

Using a system of hydrologic accounting based on Thornthwaite's method, and
taking into account the amount of moisture required for normal weather during
each month in the area in question, the departures from this normal weather
are expressed in terms of a numerical index. Positive values indicate wetter
than normal conditions while negative values represent periods of less than
normal moisture. The numerical value of the index indicates the degree of
drought as shown below.

TABLE 4

PALMER DROUGHT INDEX DEGREES OF SEVERITY[a]

Index Value	Drought Category
0	Normal (for place being analyzed)
- .50 to - .99	Incipient drought
-1.00 to -1.99	Mild drought
-2.00 to -2.99	Moderate drought
-3.00 to -3.99	Severe drought
-4.00 or less	Extreme drought

[a]Source Wayne C. Palmer, "Climatic Variability and
Crop Production," Weather and Our Food Supply, CAED Report
20 (Ames, Iowa: Center for Agricultural and Economic Development, 1964), p. 180.

If one assumes that the amount of precipitation required for a near
normal operation remains relatively stable, the month by month values com-
puted over a period of years can be used to compare the duration and relative severity of various droughts. With index values for several stations

---

[1]Wayne C. Palmer, "Meteorological Drought," Research Paper No. 45,
U. S. Weather Bureau (Washington: U. S. Department of Commerce, February,
1965), p. 1. This publication also shows in detail the mathematical deriva-
tion of the final index number.

for the same time periods one can compare the relative severity of certain droughts in different areas.

The Great Plains and Other Semi-Arid Areas

The kinds of problems faced by settlers of the Great Plains are paralleled by those of farmers in other semi-arid areas of the earth.[1] There are many striking similarities between the patterns of settlement of the Great Plains and those in other semi-arid portions of North America, Australia,[2] and South Africa. In each of these cases the settlers were mainly individuals from humid Western Europe. Some of the same problems are encountered in the virgin lands program in present-day U.S.S.R. but there state rather than individual planning is the rule.[3] In Latin America the pattern was also somewhat different since larger land grants were common and because many of the owners were already familiar with the arid conditions of Spain.

Today, with increasing population pressure and more demands on the land, the Old World steppe areas have been increasingly eyed as areas of expansion, as in the interior of China, in Kazakstan and throughout the Middle East.[4] There have been attempts to substitute settled agriculture in place of the traditional nomadism. Barth[5] effectively demonstrates some of the problems which governments face in their attempts to force or persuade the nomads to settle. Some of the world's steppelands are among the most recent

---

[1] For a broad survey of past patterns in various arid and semi-arid areas of the world, see L. D. Stamp (ed.), A History of Land Use in Arid Regions (Arid Zone Research Series, Vol. XVII; Paris: UNESCO, 1961). A review article which deals directly with the comparison of settlement in several of the semi-arid areas of the world is that of Marvin W. Mikesell, "Comparative Studies in Frontier History," Annals of the Association of American Geographers, L, No. 1 (1960), 62-74.

[2] Heathcote states that the success achieved in settling the semi-arid portions of Australia came in spite of official policies designed for the more humid portions of the country and was largely due to the more accurate assessment of resources of the experienced man on the land. R. L. Heathcote, "Conservation or Opportune Use? The Pastoralists' Problem in Semi-Arid Australia," Advancement of Science, XXI, No. 89 (1964), 47-60.

[3] A recent article discussing the Soviet adaptation is W. A. Douglas Jackson, "The Virgin and Idle Lands Program Reappraised," Annals of the Association of American Geographers, LII, No. 1 (1962), 69-79. See also his earlier article "The Virgin and Idle Lands of Western Siberia and Northern Kazakhstan: A Geographic Appraisal," Geographical Review, XLVI (1956), 492-508.

[4] A discussion of the expansion of the frontier of settled agriculture in Syria is found in N. N. Lewis, "The Frontier of Settlement in Syria: 1800-1950," International Affairs, XXXI (1951), 48-60.

[5] Fredrik Barth, "Nomadism in the Mountain and Plateau Areas of South West Asia," in UNESCO, The Problems of the Arid Zone. Proceedings of the Paris Symposium (Arid Zone Research Series Vol. XVIII; Paris: UNESCO, 1962).

large-scale frontiers of settlement.[1] They were mainly settled by people from more humid regions who started with an inaccurate perception of the possibilities and limitations of such areas, and who lacked an adapted technology for coping with the hazard of drought. The treatment of the Great Plains which follows will show how central these concepts of perception and adaptation have been and continue to be in all discussions of the area.

Past Perceptions of the Drought Hazard on the Great Plains

There has been a great deal of variation in past perceptions of the drought hazard on the Great Plains. In the first half of the nineteenth century the arid aspects were emphasized and it was known in the United States as the Great American Desert. At this time, of course, only the humid portions of the country were settled. The present name, the Great Plains, came into general usage in the post-Civil War period and Lewis suggests that the change was largely due to railroad propaganda designed to bring in settlers.[2] (For an example of promotional literature see Figure 1.) Henry Nash Smith in Virgin Land shows how the desert concept was gradually changed to fit one of the prevailing myths of the American West. This was the myth of an agricultural empire and associated imagery of the good life to be achieved in the west which Smith calls the theme of the Garden of the World. He shows how this myth was accepted as fitting the Great Plains and had a decided effect on the way Americans perceived it.[3] Such dictums as "rain follows the plow" became widely accepted by both professional and lay people. Perhaps it was this high tide of enthusiasm which left as a water mark the name Garden City, county seat of one of the present study's interview areas. A lively and well-documented article by Kollmorgen traces the origin of the belief that increasing rainfall followed settlement and the basis upon which this belief was built. Malin goes further in delineating the gradual reorientation of the

---

[1]Interesting accounts of settlement problems in several semi-arid areas of the world are provided by separate chapters in Isaiah Bowman, The Pioneer Fringe (New York: American Geographical Society, 1931).

[2]G. M. Lewis, "Changing Emphasis in the Description of the Natural Environment of the American Great Plains Area," Institute of British Geographers Publications, XXX (1962), 75-90.

[3]Henry Nash Smith, Virgin Land, the American West as Symbol and Myth (New York: Vintage Books, 1950), p. 208.

[4]Walter M. Kollmorgen, "Rainmakers on the Plains," Scientific Monthly, XL (1935), 146-152.

Actual Views in Morton County Kansas

These half-tones were made from actual photographs of the crops and products raised in Morton County, Kansas, last year (1912). They show the actual "juice," and affidavits are not necessary. Should anyone desire it we will send the name of owner and description of land upon which any one or all of these products were grown, or come and we will show you.

KANSAS

Kansas it seems to me, is not only the best pasture for all manner of beasts of the field, but it is the best field for rearing men and women. I know of no other place in civilization where a workingman's dollar will bring him so much comfort and so many benefits, expose him to so few vices and surround him with such decent mental, moral and material influences that make for character and for every manner of prosperity, as in Kansas. The human crop of Kansas is the apex of the material pyramid which has for its base cattle, and corn, and alfalfa, and hogs, and wheat and prairie grass. Upon these foundations Kansas is building men whose ideals reach to the stars. —W. A. White, Editor Emporia Gazette.

United States Senator Thompson and Lieutenant-Governor Hopkins, both of Garden City, Kansas, looking over one of Morton County's milo maize fields. These distinguished gentlemen know the general conditions in southwest Kansas, and always speak a good word for Morton

A. J. Gerber, County Treasurer, in one corner of his hundred-acre field of milo, Kaffir, corn, sorghum, broom corn and water melons. Corn made 35 bushels per acre; maize, 45 bushels, and the seed from water melons net over $35 per acre. He is one of our progressive farmers.

STOCK RAISING

Morton county has always been considered by stock-men, on account of the wonderful supply of water and the excellent growth of native grass and the ease with which the different grains can be raised, to be one of the best places in the entire southwest for the raising of all classes of stock. As a rule cattle raising has predominated and many large ranches were located in Morton county, where thousands of high grade cattle were raised on the natural grasses. Horses, mules, sheep and hogs are all raised profitably, and in the past fifteen years there has been thousands of these animals shipped to eastern markets.

Our fine climate and the open winters reduces the expense of raising stock to the very lowest minimum, and many winters the stock has ranged entirely on the rich buffalo grass without any grain or hay whatever. Owing to excellent climatic conditions, all classes of stock thrive and very seldom there is a loss.

The large ranches have all been closed out, which gives the man of moderate means an opportunity to purchase a few quarters of our land and enter into the diversified farming which is being followed profitably by hundreds in the county at the present time, and with railroad facilities many fine opportunities are to be had.

The Santa Fe railroad is considered to be one of the greatest factors in the upbuilding of a country, and the fact that this company has purchased practically 90,000 acres of land in Morton county and is building a road into the county is conclusive evidence that the country is bound to advance. After the purchase of this land by the company it is placed on the market at very reasonable prices and terms, which affords the best opportunity ever offered in southwest Kansas for the home builder. All questions along any line pertaining to the county generally will be answered.

Alfalfa field under the large artesian well, showing one of the main ditches. This alfalfa produced almost five tons to the acre last year. This crop was sowed June 20, 1911.

MORTON COUNTY

Morton County is the southwest corner county of Kansas. Owing to the location it is in one of the very best climates in the entire southwest. Very seldom there are severe storms and the winters have been known to continue without any storms whatever. This certainly makes an ideal place in which to live.

One of the very best points in favor of the county is the exceptionally healthful climate. Many people who have come here for their health have regained it from the natural conditions without medicine.

The county has a forty thousand dollar court house, all paid for, and the good management of the county in the past has kept the taxes down within reason. The taxes range from $4.50 to $6.00 per quarter section, and the levy on personal property is very low.

There is an inexhaustible supply of shallow sheet-water throughout the entire county, and a wonderful flow of artesian water has been demonstrated. The county, according to government reports, is in one of the greatest artesian water basins known. These two points being proven certainly assures the future of the county.

The rain fall, according to carefully prepared observations for over twenty-five years show that from 16 to 25 inches fall every year, therefore it will be seen that but very little water outside of this is needed to make any crop.

The Santa Fe Railroad company now has the grade through the entire county completed, which will afford the best of transportation for all crops grown. It will certainly be of interest to all who contemplate purchasing good land to come and investigate and become conversant with the great opportunities which are offered along many of the different lines. The time to come is when the country is building.

SANTA FE LANDS

The plat on other side shows all lands owned by the company which are for sale, at reasonable prices and exceptionally good terms. Prices range from $1600 to $2600 per quarter section, and terms are: one-eighth paid at time of purchase, balance in seven equal payments, last payment falling due at the end of the eighth year; second payment due at the end of the second year. Six per cent interest will be charged, and any part or all can be paid at any time and unaccrued interest rebated.

All particulars cheerfully given to anyone interested.

One of the white cane fields one mile north of Richfield. The seed alone net over $15 per acre besides the fodder for stock. This is an easy and a sure crop for our county.

A fifteen-acre field of watermelons grown by Theodore Lewis. The seed from the melons netted over $40 per acre. How is this for $13 an acre land? The large seed houses know what can be done.

Exclusive Agents for Santa Fe Lands and Town Lots in Morton County	WILSON & DEAN	RICHFIELD, KANSAS.

Fig. 1.--Sample of Great Plains Promotional Literature.
(Source: Mel Hecht Collection)

forest man's ideas about the Great Plains. He describes it in terms of a
number of phases.

> The first phase was the mistaken idea that settlement would change the
> climate, later that irrigation would neutralize it and finally that man
> must adapt his way of life to regional differences and complexities.
> This did not happen in formal stages; the threads ran through the period
> with fluctuating emphasis, but the last mentioned phase at long last be-
> came the emerging dominant point of view among informed people.[1]

One might wonder how many Plains dwellers belong to this group of informed
people. Kollmorgen and Jenks as late as the 1950s found that 95 per cent of
the class members in a Plains teachers college thought that the Shelter Belt
program would temper the winds and increase the rainfall.[2]

It is clear that certain professional people working for the government had a clear perception of the drought hazard of the Great Plains at an
early date. But it seems unlikely that this understanding was soon shared by
either the government in general or by the settlers who came in. Only too
often the settlers acted like the hero in the story which serves as an introduction to this chapter, with its classic Great Plains theme of ignorant
man versus the elements. In 1879 Powell's Report on the Arid Lands of the
United States showed an awareness of the drought hazard by suggesting classification of the land of the arid regions into three categories--forest land
above, irrigable land below and pasturage land between.[3] He advised arranging
the land divisions and future settlement pattern in conformance with the
topographic and climatic conditions.

But, as many scholars have noted, Major Powell's advice was vigorously
opposed by the decision makers, and the Great Plains was settled with the same
sort of land division as the more humid lands to the east. In the same manner,
right up to the present time, men coming into the area have continued to ignore, or at least have not acted upon, the best information available as to
the area's agricultural prospects. And because the Great Plains is a mar-
ginal area for agriculture with wet years followed by years of drought, this
lack of awareness or ignoring of the facts has led to much needless human
suffering along with the great benefits of the occasional bumper crop.

---

[1] James C. Malin, The Grassland of North America: Prolegomena to Its
History with Addenda (Lawrence, Kansas: by the author, 1961), p. 175.

[2] Walter M. Kollmorgen and George F. Jenks, "A Geographic Study of
Population and Settlement Changes in Sherman County Kansas, Part III Inventory and Prospects," Transactions, Kansas Academy of Science, LV (1952),
22.

[3] John W. Powell, Report on the Lands of the Arid Region of the
United States (Washington: U. S. Government Printing Office, 1879).

The same story has been repeated with each drought-created crisis.
After a period of expansion due to more than average amounts of rainfall,
came years of drought. And with it came the oft-repeated pattern of destitute
farmers, mobilization of relief measures, and a new government report reiter-
ating the basic fact that the Great Plains is a semi-arid area with a drought
hazard that must be heeded. Thus, the report of Willard D. Johnson, "The
High Plains and Their Utilization" followed the severe drought of the 1890s.[1]
"Dust Bowl" conditions in the 1930s were followed by the report of the Great
Committee, The Future of the Great Plains.[2] And the recent period of extended
drought, that of the early 1950s led to the publication of both"Program for
the Great Plains"[3] by the United States Department of Agriculture and more recently, Drouth,[4] a report on drought in the Great Plains and Southwest prepared under the direction of the Special Assistant to the President for Public
Works Planning.

Certain experts writing about the Great Plains have shown a fine appreciation of the drought hazard. Webb considered the water deficiency the
most essential element in explaining the differences between the Plains and

---

[1]Willard D. Johnson, "The High Plains and Their Utilization,"
United States Geological Survey, 21st Annual Report, Part IV (1899-1900),
pp. 609-741. Willard D. Johnson, "The High Plains and Their Utilization,"
United States Geological Survey, 22nd Annual Report, Part IV (1900-1901,
1902), pp. 635-669.

[2]United States Great Plains Committee, The Future of the Great
Plains (Washington: U. S. Government Printing Office, 1936). Other reports
appearing after the drought of the 30s were Francis D. Cronin and Howard W.
Beers, Areas of Intense Drought Distress, 1930-36 (Works Progress Adminis-
tration Research Bulletin, Series V, No. 1; Washington, January, 1937);
Conrad Taeuber and Carl C. Taylor, The People of the Drought States (Works
Progress Administration Research Bulletin, Series V, No. 2; Washington,
1937); Irene Link, Relief and Rehabilitation in the Drought Area (Works
Progress Administration Research Bulletin, Series V, No. 3; Washington:
June, 1937); R. S. Kifer and H. L. Stewart, Farming Hazards in the Drought
Area (Works Progress Administration Research Monograph XVI; Washington,
1938).

[3]U. S. Department of Agriculture, "Program for the Great Plains,"
U. S. Department of Agricultural Miscellaneous Publication No. 709 (Washington: U. S. Government Printing Office, 1956).

[4]Special Assistant to the President for Public Works Planning,
Drouth: A Report, A Report on Drouth in the Great Plains and the Southwest
(Washington: U. S. Government Printing Office, October, 1958). Another
series of reports on the effects of the drought of the 50s were those of
the U. S. Geological Survey including H. E. Thomas, "General Summary of
Effects on the Drouth in the Southwest," Geological Survey Professional
Paper 372-H (Washington: U. S. Government Printing Office, 1963).

the more humid eastern areas.[1] The most perceptive account of the area's
weather is found in Thornthwaite's chapter on the Great Plains in _Migration
and Economic Opportunity_ where he lucidly illustrates the climatic uncertainties and how they affect the chances for successful agriculture.

Adaptation to Great Plains Conditions

Adaptation has been another recurring theme in all major works on the
Great Plains. In _The Future of the Great Plains_ the authors state this very
clearly as follows:

> It cannot be emphasized too strongly that the success of an agricultural
> economy in the Great Plains area pivots primarily on effective adjust-
> ment to climatic conditions.[2]

Malin spoke of it as the need for harmonization of culture and environment, as the gradual change from the forest-corn culture complex to the wheat-
livestock culture.[3] Walter Prescott Webb in _The Great Plains_ stresses the key
role played by certain inventions in making possible the American habitation
of the region. The colt revolver, the windmill and barbed wire are cited as
technological innovations which enabled the white man to replace the Indian
and start Plains agriculture. Rather than certain key inventions Malin emphasized the role of technology in making possible the cheap production and rapid
diffusion of these implements.[4] His _Winter Wheat in the Golden Belt of Kansas_
illustrates his contention that the process of adaptation to the environmental
exigencies is not just the result of a few major inventions but is a folk-
process consisting of the gradual accumulation of innumerable smaller modifications made by the farmers themselves.[5] He calls for a reconciliation of
science and the folk-process. Support for the value of the folk-process in
this type of adaptation can be found in a remarkably similar tale told by
Meinig about the wheatlands of South Australia in _On the Margins of the Good_

---

[1] Walter Prescott Webb, _The Great Plains_ (New York: Grosset and
Dunlap, by arrangement with Ginn & Company, 1931).

[2] United States Great Plains Committee, p. 33.

[3] Malin, p. 328.

[4] James C. Malin, "The Grassland of North America: Its Occupance and
the Challenge of Continuous Reappraisals," _Man's Role in Changing the Face
of the Earth_, ed. William L. Thomas, Jr. (Chicago: University of Chicago
Press, 1956), pp. 350-366.

[5] James C. Malin, _Winter Wheat in the Golden Belt of Kansas_ (Lawrence:
University of Kansas Press, 1944).

Earth.[1] There, as in Kansas, there was a proliferation of implemental innovation to overcome each newly-perceived environmental obstacle.

With improvements in technology come new methods for coping with the
drought hazard. Experience gained in each of the major droughts might be expected to result in further progress toward more adapted farming. Many observers have commented on the continually increasing size of farms made
necessary by the risks of the area and made possible by improved tractors
and implements. Kollmorgen and Jenks, writing just before the major drought
of the 1950s, mention a whole series of innovations during the 1940s in Sherman County, Kansas.[2] Hewes analyzed the reasons for the reduction of wheat
failure in Western Nebraska from 1931-1937 to 1938-1954.[3] In addition to
slightly better fall moisture he lists as major factors in reducing wheat
losses the increasing use of summer fallow, better control of blowing, ac-
cumulated experience, perhaps the greater use of power and adapted machinery,
and reduced grasshopper damage. In a recent study in Eastern Colorado
Bowden traces the diffusion of another type of adjustment, pump irrigation.[4]

In addition to dry farming techniques and improved machinery a wide
range of institutional adjustments and management strategies are necessary
to improve man's adaptation to the Great Plains. Kraenzel's comprehensive
book, The Great Plains in Transition, describes the basic problems and current
adaptations with particular emphasis on improved institutional arrangements
specially suited to the regional conditions of semi-aridity. He states that,

> For civilization to survive and thrive in the Plains three basic traits
> are necessary--reserves, flexibility and mobility. These traits need to

---

[1]Donald W. Meinig, On the Margins of the Good Earth, AAG Monograph
Series (Chicago: Rand McNally & Co., 1962).

[2]Kollmorgen and Jenks, p. 36.

[3]The work of Hewes using wheat failure as an index of risk in the
Central Great Plains has resulted in the following series of four articles
with more forthcoming: Leslie Hewes and Arthur C. Schmieding, "Geographi-
cal Patterns of Wheat Failure in Nebraska, 1931-1952," Geographical Review,
XLVI (1956), 375-387; Leslie Hewes, "Wheat Failure in Western Nebraska, 1931-
1954," Annals of the Association of American Geographers, XLVIII (1958), 375-
397; Leslie Hewes, "A Traverse Across Kit Carson County, Colorado, with
Notes on Land Use on the Margin of the Old Dust Bowl, 1939-1940 and 1962,"
Economic Geography, XXXIX (1963), 332-340; and Lewlie Hewes, "Causes of
Wheat Failure in the Dry Farming Region, Central Great Plains, 1939-1957,"
Economic Geography, XLI (1965), 313-330.

[4]Leonard W. Bowden, Diffusion of the Decision to Irrigate, Simula-
tion of the Spread of a New Resource Management Practice in the Colorado
Northern High Plains, Department of Geography Research Paper No. 75,
University of Chicago (Chicago: Department of Geography, 1962).

become ingrained in all forms of activity, especially the more vital
and costly institutional patterns of the region.[1]

Reserves, both individual and corporate, are necessary to cushion the effects
of the extreme fluctuations in yield and income. Flexibility, the ability
and willingness to adjust to change, is required to overcome instability due
to semi-aridity.[2] It involves such things as a credit system with flexible
repayment periods, ability in individual farm operations to shift from one
kind of production to another, more flexible farm implements and adapted
crops and flexible arrangements for public health care, taxation policies
and education. Mobility allows the farmer to overcome the great distances
and gain by timeliness of operations. It aids in avoiding complete hail or
drought loss by enabling farmers to work land in several different locations,
many miles apart, or by moving livestock to separate summer and winter ranges.

The search for more adapted management strategies is illustrated by the
recent work of a Great Plains Research Committee. Publications resulting
from a workshop in Lincoln, Nebraska, in 1959[3] and a symposium at Bozeman,
Montana, in 1962[4] describe current thinking on this topic. A review of the
work under way, leading toward extension and revision is being prepared by
Bailey of the Economic Research Service of the United States Department of
Agriculture.[5] In it is outlined a list of strategies currently being studied.
Some of these are institutional arrangements, production technologies, enterprise choice, flexible livestock systems, feed reserves, off-farm employment,
contract farming, financial management and spatial diversification.

In addition to changing the environment and the institutional and
economic arrangements, another possible type of adaptation is that of a
change in basic attitudes and personality characteristics. There have been

---

[1]Kraenzel, The Great Plains in Transition, p. 324.

[2]A very good discussion of various types of flexibility in the practi-
cal farming situation is that by Emery N. Castle, "Adapting Western Kansas
Farms to Uncertain Prices and Yields," Kansas State College Agricultural
Experiment Station Technical Bulletin 75 (Manhattan, 1954).

[3]Great Plains Research Technical Committee GP-2, Management Strategies
in Great Plains Farming, Proceedings of a Workshop Held by Great Plains
Research Technical Committee GP-2 Lincoln, Nebraska, May 5-7, 1959 (Lincoln:
Great Plains Council Publication No. 19, August, 1961).

[4]Great Plains Research Technical Committee GP-2, Economic Problems
in Great Plains Ranching, GP-2 Symposium Bozeman May 23-24, 1962 (Bozeman:
Great Plains Council Publication No. 22, October, 1964).

[5]Warren R. Bailey, "Organizing and Operating Dryland Farms in the
Plains Environment," Summary of Regional Research Project GP-2, review
draft. (Ditto.)

a few speculative accounts of the extent to which this has occurred in the
Great Plains but no thorough studies to date. Consideration of the personality characteristics within such a region raises the old spectre of environmental determinism to be treated a little further in the next chapter. The
question of whether the impersonal physical environment has any marked effect
on personality has never really been settled conclusively. If such effects do
occur, however, it seems likely that the very stressful Great Plains environment[1] would be one in which distinct personality traits could occur, either
through a selection process in terms of who comes and stays or through a
process of change within the area. It has been common to posit certain attitudes, ideas and traits as characteristic of Great Plains people.

Franklin Thomas in The Environmental Basis of Society[2] reviews the
literature related to the effect of the environment on man. In his final
chapter he summarized some of the theories which, though unproven and untested, have survived the entire span of Western Civilization. Those of
relevance to the Great Plains environment are: that man in order to be
vigorous and brave needs a climate which demands fortitude and exertion,
the environment must supply enough obstacles to stimulate effort but not
enough to discourage the people; that isolation leads to bravery and ruggedness but also to political and cultural backwardness; geographic factors are
more important in primitive society but with the advance of civilization the
importance of psychological and cultural factors increases. In the light of
these theories some of the scattered statements which have been made about
Great Plainsmen will be examined.

Because of both the stressful environment and isolation one would
expect Great Plainsmen to be vigorous, brave and rugged. And most of those
who have discussed their personality characteristics have tended to emphasize this in one way or another. A good example is Vance Johnson in Heaven's
Tableland who wrote of the necessary mixture of grit and foolhardiness required to stick it out,[3] of the grim sort of humor developed around dust,[4]

---

[1]The important factor here is, not simply the fact of living in an area
of climatic stress, but that the Great Plains wheat farmer's success in his
role in society is geared to his productivity in terms of wheat and this is dependent on the vagaries of the weather. Other people living in the area, with
less dependence on climatic conditions, would be less likely to be affected.

[2]Franklin Thomas, The Environmental Basis of Society: A Study in the
History of Sociological Theory (New York and London, 1925). Reprint by
Johnson Reprint Corporation, 1965.

[3]Vance Johnson, Heaven's Tableland (New York: Farrar, Straus &
Co., 1947), p. 191.

[4]Ibid., p. 193.

and of the "Last Man's Club."[1] The latter was started by the then editor of
the Dalhart Texan who made a pledge and published it. He was going to stay
until everyone else was gone--until he was the last man. He dared others to
join him. And although this club held no meetings, charged no dues, and
adopted no resolutions, applications for memberships poured in from all over
the Plains, an indication of its grass roots acceptance. Others who have
emphasized a similar ruggedness, brave spirit and determination are Bennett
who mentioned the manly ethos and frontier spirit of those in Southwestern
Saskatchewan;[2] and Edwards writing about Haskell County, Kansas, suggested
that adventurous people were attracted to the area.[3] He stressed their ir-
repressible determination, and ability to swing from pessimism to optimism
with extreme rapidity.[4] On the other hand, it may be that the climate is
too stressful so that, as Gordon asserts, they tend to resign themselves to
the idea that success in raising a crop is due to fate and luck.[5]

Kraenzel's discussion from a basically sociological point of view
would support the idea that the isolation, or hinterland status, has led to
political backwardness.[6] He describes the set of attitudes and behavior patterns developed by residents as minority conduct. Some characteristics of
this conduct are people "on the prod" willing to fight at the drop of the
hat, schisms preventing union for broader action, and emotions too deeply
rooted for rational actions. An example of cultural backwardness resulting
from isolation is given by Bennett and Kohl in explaining the ambivalent
attitude toward education for their sons which is held by ranchers, and
their distrust of formal rationality.[7]

---

[1]Ibid., p. 197.

[2]John W. Bennett, "Synopsis of a Cultural Ecology Research Program
in Saskatchewan," Plains Anthropologist, VIII, No. 20 (1963), 88.

[3]A. D. Edwards, Influence of Drought and Depression on a Rural Community, A Case Study in Haskell County, Kansas, the Farm Security Administration and the Bureau of Agricultural Economics cooperating (Social Research Report No. VII; Washington, D.C.: January, 1939), p. 91.

[4]Ibid., p. 93.

[5]Ira J. Gordon, "The Kansas Wheat Culture," Transactions, Kansas
Academy of Science, LV (1952), 56.

[6]Kraenzel, The Great Plains in Transition, chap. xvii.

[7]John W. Bennett and Seena Kohl, "Two Memoranda on Social Organization and Adaptive Selection in a Northern Plains Region," Plains Anthropologist, VII, No. 22 (1964), 10-22.

Some of the results of Bennett's studies indicate that environmental factors are not as important in the Great Plains as they might be in a more primitive society. He states that there are three main pressures on the individual, namely, kinfolk, the manly ethos, and the exigencies of the environment. Some of the social pressures are elaborated on in a description of the "Bound-dependent" relationship, resulting from the dependency of a young man on either his father or an established rancher for help in starting out, and how this dependent relationship may be prolonged indefinitely. This results in the selection or development of two main types according to Bennett. The first is a passive dependent type who is cheerful, loyal, hard-working, passive, able to defer gratifications and conforms to local rules. The second is the aggressive conformer who accepts the role as a challenge and tries to become as independent as possible as soon as possible. The former type is believed by Bennett to be by far the most common.

Though suggestive and perhaps useful as working hypotheses, the above comments on personality characteristics of Great Plains farmers are generally unsystematic, untested, and basically by-products of studies focussing on other aspects of the Great Plains problem. However, they should help to set the stage for discussion of some personality characteristics of Great Plains wheat farmers in chapter vii.

The drought hazard on the Great Plains and the way it has been perceived and reacted to has been the focus of this chapter's discussion. Webb, referring to the line between the humid east and the semi-arid Great Plains, had this to say:

> When people first crossed this line they did not immediately realize the imperceptible change that had taken place in their environment, nor, more is the tragedy, did they foresee the full consequences which that change was to bring in their own characters and in their modes of life. In the new region--level, timberless and semiarid--they were thrown by Mother Necessity into a new clutch of circumstances.[1]

Here he has combined all the elements considered above; the unique environment of the Great Plains with its drought hazard, the problem of perception of this unfamiliar environment, and the adaptations both in way of life and in personality characteristics which have resulted.

---

[1]Webb, p. 9.

CHAPTER II

THE ROLE OF PERCEPTION IN RESOURCE MANAGEMENT

Boy that's your 30s weather. That's a drought year. Boy how
familiar that looks. Man walking across the field and it's desolate
and drifting. But he's looking down at his soil and he knows it's
good and it's there. He knows that if he gets over this bad weather,
the soil is there and ready to produce. And it worked out like that.

The problem of how men in the Great Plains perceive the drought
hazard is inextricably entangled with the larger more general question of
environmental perception. And the problem of how men perceive their environment is part of the larger system of man and environment which has always
been a major concern of geography. This chapter begins at the broadest level,
the man-environment tradition in geography. It shows how the recent interest of geographers and others in environmental perception is related to this
tradition. The range of interest in perception and the man-milieu relationship is suggested to demonstrate that this new research frontier is not just
confined to geography but is evident in many of the behavioral sciences.[1]
With this background given, the focus of discussion narrows to the problem
of perception in geography. Some of the more provocative studies of environmental perception and adaptation from fields other than geography are
reviewed. This is followed by consideration of the kinds of approaches to
perceptual studies in the field of natural resources which have been utilized to date. There is a final focusing on the research tradition most
relevant to the present study, that is, the flood plains studies and their

---

[1]Environmental perception fits all the requirements for placing
geography on a research frontier as set out by Edward A. Ackerman, "Where
Is a Research Frontier," Annals of the Association of American Geographers,
LIII, No. 4 (1963), 429-440. The four general requirements are: 1. strength-
en quantifying methods, 2. recognize an earth-wide man-environment system
as our overriding problem, 3. choose research problems in light of the ad-
vancing frontier of the behavioral sciences, and with attention to systems-
oriented study in the neighboring earth sciences, 4. new supplementary approaches.

derivatives concerned with man's perception of natural hazards. The chapter concludes with suggestions of needed future research and the relation of the present study to these needs.

The Man-Environment Tradition in Geography

The man-environment relationship has a rich tradition in geography. Some forty odd years ago Harlan H. Barrows recommended studying geography as human ecology, that is, by focusing on the study of human adjustment to specific natural environments.[1] Sixty years earlier George Perkins Marsh in his Man and Nature; or, Physical Geography as Modified by Human Action showed the intricate linkages and far-reaching effects of man's actions on the earth.[2] The symposium volume dedicated to Marsh, Man's Role in Changing the Face of the Earth, brings up to date in a comprehensive fashion the myriad subtle and direct ways in which man alters the physical environment.[3]

However, American geography in recent years has shown a relative neglect of the other side of the coin, the earth's role in changing the face of man, despite an equally hoary tradition stretching back as far as man's written works. Thomas in The Environmental Basis of Society reviewed the major works along this line showing how certain themes have persisted through the centuries. Ratzel outlined the framework, a set of categories of the types of environmental influences on men. These are listed by Semple as (1) direct physical effects (especially climate), (2) psychical effects as reflected in religion, literature, modes of thought and figures of speech, (3) economic and social effects due to the general character of natural resources, and (4) effects upon movements of people due to the influence of geographic features, i.e., barriers or channels of easy access.[4] Rostlund in a delightful article entitled "Twentieth Century Magic" shows how pervasive environmentalism is in the present both within and outside geography

---

[1]Harlan H. Barrows, "Geography as Human Ecology," Annals of the Association of American Geographers, XIII (1923), 1-14. For an up-to-date discussion of the same concept see D. R. Stoddart, "Geography and the Ecological Approach The Ecosystem as a Geographic Principle and Method," Geography, L, Part 3 (1965), 242-251.

[2]George Perkins Marsh, Man and Nature; or, Physical Geography as Modified by Human Action (New York: Scribner, Armstrong and Company, 1864).

[3]William L. Thomas, Jr. (ed.), Man's Role in Changing the Face of the Earth (Chicago: University of Chicago Press, 1956).

[4]Ellen C. Semple, Influences of the Geographic Environment (New York: Henry Holt & Company, 1911), chap. ii.

and suggests that geographers should take another look at environmentalist notions since they were really "not disproved, only disapproved."[1]

The Sprouts in considering this question asserted that:

> It is quite impossible to answer the questions "what" and "where" with respect to any complex state-of-affairs without becoming involved to some extent with the questions of "how" and "why." The moment one admits these latter questions, even if only by implication, he introduces some hypothesis of the relationship between the actors and the setting, or milieu, in which they carry on.[2]

If we accept their statement it behooves us to examine the range of man-milieu hypotheses which they outline. The first is that of environmental determinism which essentially is the idea that environmental factors are all-powerful, that they determine what happens and man really has no choice regardless of what he may think. The second and quite similar hypothesis is mild environmentalism which differs in that while Nature is all-powerful man can choose, at his own peril, to disregard the environmental directives. The third, environmental possibilism is concerned with the possibilities and limitations set by the environment and does not consider human motivations or criteria of choice. The fourth, probabilism is the explanation or prediction of the typical person's reaction to a given milieu on the basis of a genalized model whose reliability depends on the analyst's own knowledge and insight. The fifth hypothesis is cognitive behaviorism which assumes that a person reacts to his milieu as he perceives and interprets it in the light of his previous experience. This final hypothesis is the one embodied in most of the current work on a perception in geography. Since the person's actions vis-à-vis the environment are assumed to depend on his perception of the environment it becomes important to find out just how it is perceived.

Relation to Other Behavioral Sciences

Examples of interest in perception and man-milieu relationships can be found in a wide variety of behavioral sciences for how people come to know and interpret their world is fundamental to an understanding of human behavior.

---

[1] Erhard Rostlund, "Twentieth Century Magic," Readings in Cultural Geography, ed. Philip L. Wagner and Marvin W. Mikesell (Chicago and London: University of Chicago Press, 1962), pp. 48-53.

[2] Harold and Margaret Sprout, Man-Milieu Relationship Hypotheses in the Context of International Politics (Princeton, N.J.: Princeton University Center of International Studies, 1956), p. 20. This essay has been expanded considerably in a later revision which includes many examples of each type of hypothesis. Harold and Margaret Sprout, The Ecological Perspective On Human Affairs with Special Reference to International Politics (Princeton, N.J.: Princeton University Press, 1965).

The examples which follow are intended to be suggestive rather than inclusive and reflect the writer's own rambling readings rather than a rigorous framework.

Psychologists have probably spent more time considering the problem of perception than any other group of investigators. This is reflected in the wide variety of different theories of perception currently being advanced by psychologists specializing in this subfield of psychology.[1] Some of the early work started from the basic notion that all knowledge of the world depends on the senses and their stimulation. The main concern was with the functioning of the sense organs and their sensitivity to various levels of stimulation. This kind of work continues with the modern psychophysicists. A more recent definition of perception is that of Bereleson and Steiner, "process by which people select, organize, and interpret sensory stimulation into a meaningful and coherent picture of the world."[2] This definition reflects what has been insisted upon by later work in the field, namely, that perception is a function not only of the stimulus present and the capabilities of the sense organs but also of past learning and motivation. This change of emphasis can be seen in much of the recent work in social psychology.

In social psychology there are several active groups of experimenters working on perception problems. Jerome Bruner goes so far as to say "contemporary social psychology . . . is much concerned, indeed even preoccupied, with problems of perception."[3] Some examples of the types of studies pursued are the effects of a frame of reference on perception as illustrated by the studies of Sherif employing the autokinetic effect;[4] the effects of needs as in experiments in which hungry subjects showed an increase in food related responses;[5] the effects of values on the recognition of words briefly presented

---

[1]One recent book evaluates some 13 perceptual theories and formalized the author's own views. See Floyd H. Allport, Theories of Perception and the Concept of Structure (New York: Wiley, 1955). For a briefer, more readable examination of the theories of perception, see William Bevan, "Perception: Evolution of a Concept," Psychological Review, LXV, No. 1 (1958), 34-55.

[2]B. Bereleson and G. Steiner, Human Behavior, An Inventory of Scientific Findings (New York: Harcourt, Brace & World, 1964). Chap. iv of this book is titled "Perceiving and Attempts to Summarize in an Organized Form Current Knowledge on the Subject of Perception."

[3]Jerome S. Bruner, "Social Psychology and Perception" in Readings in Social Psychology, ed. Maccoby, Newcomb, and Hartley (New York: Holt, Rinehart & Winston, Inc., 1958), pp. 85-94.

[4]M. Sherif, The Psychology of Social Norms (New York: Harper & Brothers, 1936).

[5]D. C. McClelland and J. W. Atkinson, "The Projective Expression of Needs: I. The Effect of Different Intensities of the Hunger Drive on Per-

in a fast-exposure apparatus (tachistoscope);[1] and the effects of social
norms on perception.[2] Many new insights in the effects of needs and motivation on the perceptual process have resulted from such research in the psychology laboratory but there has also been some criticism of the artificial
conditions as below:

> . . . the majority of investigators in this field have been interested
> in perception as it occurs in dark rooms and at exposure times of frac-
> tions of a second. The stimuli perceived usually are geometrical figures,
> numbers, letters, or words. The subjects, of course, are university
> students. The factors studied most commonly are stimulus factors. Psy-
> chologists in the past have been more interested in spatial relations
> than in social relations, more concerned with sensory interaction than
> with interaction between persons.[3]

One approach which would not be subject to such objections is that advocated
by MacLeod. He suggests using the phenomenological method which is the attempt to view phenomena in their entirety and without prejudice, to let the
phenomena themselves dictate the conceptual framework and the further course
of inquiry.[4] As an example he speaks of psychological geography which would
attempt to see what is there for the individual, what kind of conceptions
are actually held about different places.

A parallel development in anthropology has been an increasing
tendency to shift from a categorization in Western terms to a concern with
the local people's perception of the world. Malinowski's The Coral Gardens
and Their Magic was a pioneer work of this type.[5] In describing the garden-
ing activities of the Trobrianders he states that the actual botanical facts
do not matter as much as the process of growth seen through native eyes.
This type of approach is that advocated by anthropologists presently working
in the field of cultural ecology, as illustrated by a recent article by

---

ception," Journal of Psychology, XXV (1948), 205-222.

[1]L. Postman, J. S. Bruner, and E. McGinnies, "Personal Values as
Selective Factors in Perception," Journal of Abnormal and Social Psychology,
XXCIII (1948), 148-153.

[2]S. E. Asch, "Effects of Group Pressure upon the Modification and
Distortion of Judgments," in Readings in Social Psychology, p . 174-183.

[3]Wayne Dennis, "Cultural and Developmental Factors in Perception,"
in Perception An Approach to Personality, ed. Robert R. Blake, and Glenn V.
Ramsey (New York: The Ronald Press, 1951), chap. vi, pp. 148-169.

[4]R. B. MacLeod, "The Phenomenological Approach to Social Psychology,"
Psychological Review, LIV (1947), 193-210.

[5]Bronislaw Malinowski, The Coral Gardens and Their Magic (2 vols.;
New York, Cincinnati and Chicago: American Book Company, 1935).

Frake,[1] who says that productive ethnographies must tap the cognitive world of one's informants. A good example of this type is Harold Conklin's Hanunoo Agriculture,[2] in which the investigator uses linguistic evidence as one of the tools to study the Hanunoo concepts of ecology and methods of farming. Other people have pointed out the importance of language in organizing our thoughts and ways of viewing the external world.[3]

Psychoanalysis has in the past thirty years shown a shift in emphasis from a genetic and biological framework with emphasis on the individual to ego psychology with its greater emphasis on social character as formed by the interaction between man and his environment. This new focus of interest on social character has led to increasing interest in the environment.[4] Erikson,[5] Kardiner,[6] Fromm,[7] Horney[8] and Sullivan[9] all emphasize the role of the social environment. Kardiner goes further to show the importance of the natural or physical environment:

> . . . external reality is of two kinds; that which concerns the natural
> environment and the specific problems of adaptation that each brings
> with it and the institutional systems which in each culture makes such

---

[1]Charles O. Frake, "Cultural Ecology and Ethnography," American Anthropologist, LXIV, No. 1 (1962), 53-59. See also "Transcultural Studies in Cognition," American Anthropologist, Vol. LVI, No. 3, Part 2 (1964).

[2]Harold Conklin, Hanunoo Agriculture, Forestry Development Paper No. 12 (Rome: FAO of United Nations, 1957), and Harold C. Conklin, "An Ethnoecological Approach to Shifting Agriculture," in Readings in Cultural Geography, ed. Philip L. Wagner and Marvin W. Mikesell (Chicago: University of Chicago Press, 1962), pp. 457-464.

[3]See for example, Benjamin Lee Whorf, "Science and Linguistics," in Readings in Social Psychology, pp. 1-9.

[4]A useful study which discusses the various schools of psychoanalytic thought includes as one of the five major categories for comparison "the terms of the milieu." The thoughts of each of the major psychoanalytic theorists on the influence of the environment are considered under this category. See, Ruth L. Munroe, Schools of Psychoanalytic Thought (New York: The Dryden Press, 1955), chaps. iv and ix.

[5]Erik H. Erikson, Childhood and Society (New York: W. W. Norton & Co., 1950).

[6]A. Kardiner, The Individual and His Society (New York: Columbia University Press, 1939). See also, The Psychological Frontiers of Society (New York: Columbia University Press, 1945).

[7]E. Fromm, Escape from Freedom (New York: Farrar & Rinehart, 1941).

[8]K. Horney, The Neurotic Personality of Our Time (New York: W. W. Norton & Co., 1937).

[9]H. S. Sullivan, The Interpersonal Theory of Psychiatry (New York: W. W. Norton & Co., 1953).

different types of demands upon the individual. The adjustment required by different environmental realities and those created by the mores that govern human relationships must in each culture produce different end results in the personality, such as different thought processes and sequences, and different fantasy life.[1]

Erikson, stressing the importance of social prototypes, suggests that to study a particular person one should correlate the patient's childhood history with a history of the family's sendentary residence in prototypical areas.[2] The kind of thinking illustrated here by Kardiner and Erikson has led to a broad interdisciplinary approach[3] utilizing ideas and insights of sociologists, anthropologists, and psychoanalysts in an attempt to work out the relationships between the environment, the social institutions, and individual psychodynamics.[4]

In the field of developmental psychology the old heredity versus environment controversy has shifted from ideas of fixed intelligence and predetermined development to greater emphasis on interaction between the individual and his environment. A good review of the literature on this topic is found in Hunt's Intelligence and Experience.[5] He summarizes recent research from four major research traditions: (1) problem-solving behavior, (2) programming of electronic computers, (3) neuropsychology, and (4) the work of Piaget on the intellectual development in children.[6] All appear to point to a new concept of intelligence as a problem-solving capacity based

---

[1] Kardiner, The Individual and His Society, p. 127.

[2] E. Erikson, "Ego Development and Historical Change," Psychoanalytic Study of the Child, II, 359-395.

[3] C. Kluckhohn and H. A. Murray (ed.), "Personality Formation: the Determinants," in Personality in Nature, Society and Culture (New York: Knopf, 1953), pp. 53-67.

[4] There are some criticisms of this approach such as those by Lindesmith and Strauss who flatly state that the interdisciplinary nature is sharply limited. They also state that "Positive generalizations made in this area are generally based upon unwarranted confidence in rather loose unscientific methods of interpreting data, and upon a relatively uncritical acceptance of a particular conceptual scheme." Alfred R. Lindesmith and Anselm L. Strauss, "A Critique of Culture-Personality Writings," American Sociological Review, XV (1950), 587-600. Also reprinted as S172 in The Bobbs-Merrill Reprint Series in the Social Sciences.

[5] J. McVickers Hunt, Intelligence and Experience (New York: Ronald Press, 1961).

[6] Jean Piaget, The Child's Conception of the World (Patterson, N.J.: Littlefield, Adams & Co., 1960), p. 332. For good summaries of the work of Piaget, see Hunt above, and Kessen and Kuhlman, "Symposium on Thought in Young Children," Monograph for Society of Research in Child Development, Vol. XXVII, No. 2 (1962), especially Inholder article.

on hierarchically organized symbolic representation resulting from past experience. One problem raised by some of the experiments of Piaget is that of
rural-urban differences in the duration of various stages of the child's
cognitive development. He attributes it to differences in the amount of
direct experience with the facts of nature. A delightful personal account
of the development of the basic modes of perceptual relatedness is that of
Schachtel in Metamorphosis, where he shows the gradual change from subject-
centered to object-centered perception.[1]

This rather rapid survey of a few of the behavioral sciences shows
that not only are perceptual studies found in a wide range of fields but also
that there is an increasing trend toward this type of work. I would suggest
that the reason why this is so is because perception is a key concept in
understanding man's adaptation to his environment, both physical and social.[2]

Perception in Geography: General Statements, Theory, Suggestions

Perception is not an entirely new idea within geography. Cultural
geographers have long been concerned with it under the name of cultural appraisal. Alexander Spoehr's discussion of cultural differences in the interpretation of natural resources clearly shows how close the two concepts are.[3]
Glacken traced the changing ideas and attitudes toward the earth from the
earliest written work to the present.[4] However, the cultural geographers
have mainly used the idea in considering the perceptions of people from far
away or long ago.[5] The idea of cultural appraisal or environmental percep-

---

[1]Ernest G. Schactel, Metamorphosis (New York: Basic Books, 1959).

[2]According to Klein the ego puts perception to work in reality ap-
praisal to help the organism in seeking equilibrium between two sources of
tension, its inner strivings and the demands of reality. George S. Klein,
"The Personal World Through Perception," in Perception, An Approach to
Personality, ed. Robert R. Blake and Glenn V. Ramsey (New York: The Ronald
Press, 1951), pp. 328-355.

[3]Alexander Spoehr, "Cultural Differences in the Interpretation of
Natural Resources," Man's Role in Changing the Face of Earth, pp. 93-102.

[4]Clarence J. Glacken, "Changing Ideas of the Habitable World,"
Man's Role in Changing the Face of the Earth, pp. 70-92.

[5]For a recent example of the use of perception in cultural geography,
see Hill's discussion of the differing perceptions of the Indians and
Ladinos. David A. Hill, The Changing Landscape of a Mexican Municipio: Villa
Las Rosas, Chiapas, Department of Geography Research Paper No. 91, University
of Chicago (Chicago: 1964), pp. 100-105.

tion has, until fairly recently, been used in geography in a rather broad, general and quite subjective way to describe whole cultures. The cultural appraisal has been inferred after the fact from actual resource use patterns. It is only lately that geographers have become introspective enough to apply it to themselves or to use it as a research technique for studying individuals or groups of individuals within their own society.

The earliest methodological discussion along the lines of the present conception of perception in geography was that by Kirk in which he discussed the concept of the behavioral environment as a solution to the "creeping paralysis of possibilism."[1] He suggested thinking of a region in its dynamic aspect as a "gestalt," a whole which is something more than the sum of its parts. He was agitating toward a more workable concept of the man-milieu relationship and helped develop the idea of cognitive behaviorism previously mentioned.

Two works most valuable for their rich content and suggestiveness are Geographie Psychologique by Max Sorre[2] and David Lowenthal's "Geography, Experience and Imagination: Towards a Geographic Epistemology."[3] Sorre's monograph is divided into three sections. The first describes the milieu. Then the effects of the milieu on the individual and the group are discussed in turn. Sorre shows how little we know about these things and suggests that perhaps we need new types of instruments to measure some of the most significant aspects of the milieu in terms of effect on the individual and the group.[4] Lowenthal says:

> My epistemological inquiry . . . is concerned with all geographical
> thought, scientific and other: how it is acquired, transmitted,

---

[1]William Kirk, "Historical Geography and the Concept of the Behavioral Environment," Indian Geographical Journal, Silver Jubilee Edition, ed. George Kuriyan (Madras: Indian Geographical Society, 1952), pp. 152-160. See also, William Kirk, "Problems of Geography," Geography, XLVII, Part 4 (1963), 357-371.

[2]Max Sorre, Geographie Psychologique, Traité de Psychologie Appliquée, Livre VI, Conditions et Règles de Vie (Paris: Presses Universitaire de France, 1955).

[3]David Lowenthal, "Geography, Experience and Imagination: Towards a Geographical Epistemology," Annals of the Association of American Geographers, LI, No. 3 (1961), 241-260.

[4]A recent attempt to examine some of the variables involved in arid areas are the companion volumes: UNESCO, Environmental Physiology and Psychology in Arid Conditions: Reviews of Research, Arid Zone Research XXI (Paris, UNESCO, 1963), and UNESCO, Environmental Physiology and Psychology in Arid Conditions: Proceedings of the Lucknow Symposium, Arid Zone Research XXIV (Paris: UNESCO, 1964).

altered, and integrated into conceptual syst.... and how the horizon
of geography varies among individuals and g... [1]

He suggests that our ideas and images of the world are compounded of memory,
imagination and experience, and gives examples of how they apparently vary
in children, primitives, psychotics, animals and normal people. Again the
impression is given that more remains to be discovered than has thus far been
investigated.

Yi Fu Tuan and Joseph Sonnenfeld have actively advanced ideas which
involve use of perception in geography. Tuan called for more perceptive,
sensitive portrayals of the earth by geographers and has discussed the symbolic significance of certain landscapes for Western man.[2] Sonnenfeld used
the framework of adaptation level theory to evaluate measures of environmental attitude and sensitivity among a number of arctic populations in
Alaska.[3] He emphasized the sources of perceptual variability. His research
indicates that the way in which environmental attributes are perceived is a
function of culture, economy, personality and experience as well as individual
and racial physiology, all of which will condition the perception of the stimulus and thus the adaptation level determining the individual's sensitivity
to that stimulus.

One other recent suggestion which falls within the realm of perception in geography was that made by Sister Mary Annette in her methodological
inquiry in social geography.[4] She indicated the need for more attention to
what she called "the psychic factor," space and distance as perceived by
human occupants of countries or regions. She suggests that it might be
fruitful to adopt the French concept of "l'espace social" as a framework
for such studies.

---

[1]Lowenthal, *Annals of the Association of American Geographers*, LI,
241, fn. 2.

[2]Yi Fu Tuan, "Topophilia or Sudden Encounter with the Landscape,"
Landscape, XI (Autumn, 1961), 29-32; Yi Fu Tuan, "Attitudes Toward Environ-
ment: Themes and Approaches," Paper presented at 61st Annual Meeting of
Association of American Geographers at Columbus, Ohio, April 20, 1965; also
"The Problem of Geographic Description," Paper presented at 60th Annual
Meeting of the Association of American Geographers, Syracuse, New York,
March 29-April 1, 1964. For further discussion of the latter point, see
H. C. Darby, "The Problem of Geographical Description," *Transactions and
Papers: The Institute of British Geographers*, No. 30 (1962), pp. 1-13.

[3]Joseph Sonnenfeld, "Environmental Perception and Adaptation Level
in the Arctic," Paper presented at 61st Annual Meeting of Association of
American Geographers at Columbus, Ohio, April 20, 1965.

[4]Sister Mary Annette, "Social Geography: Some Methodological
Considerations," Paper presented at 61st Annual Meeting of Association of
American Geographers at Columbus, Ohio, April 21, 1965.

Environmental Perception and Adaptation: Relevant
Work from Other Fields

Several provocative studies directly concerned with environmental perception and adaptation have been made by persons outside of geography. Lynch's The Image of the City describes techniques developed for investigating the imageability of the city and elements used by people in orienting themselves in an urban area.[1] The implication is that by determining how people perceive the urban environment one can better approach the problem of planning to create a city with a vital and coherent image. In some later work these ideas have been amplified and extended in an investigation of the visual qualities of roads.[2] An entirely different contribution but equally relevant to the field of environmental perception and adptation is the book of Rogers, The Diffusion of Innovations.[3] Rogers, a rural sociologist, draws together the pertinent literature from several different fields. A theoretical framework is set up to show what is known about the way in which ideas (innovations) are communicated from person to person within a social system over time. In discussing the adoption process he speaks of a series of stages or steps as follows: awareness, interest, evaluation, trial and adoption. The first three of these stages would roughly correspond to what is called perception in this study. Rogers also classifies individuals within a social system on the basis of innovativeness. The adopter categories whose distribution Rogers defines according to the normal curve are innovators, early adopters, early majority, late majority and laggards. Each of these have distinct characteristics and different roles in the communication process.

Two other studies by anthropologists have been directly concerned with the adaptation process in an arid environment. The first, a large scale project under the auspices of Harvard University, is "The Comparative Study of Values in Five Cultures."[4] In New Mexico where five distinct cul-

---

[1] Kevin Lynch, The Image of the City (Cambridge, Mass.: Technology Press and Harvard University Press, 1960.

[2] Donald Appleyard, Kevin Lynch and John R. Myer, The View from the Road (Cambridge: M.I.T. Press, 1964).

[3] Everett M. Rogers, Diffusion of Innovations (New York: The Free Press of Glencoe, 1962).

[4] The volume from this series which is most directly applicable here is Evon S. Vogt, Modern Homesteaders: The Life of a Twentieth Century Frontier Community (Cambridge: The Balknap Press of Harvard University Press, 1955).

ture groups are found within one comparatively small area they investigated
the effects of different value systems on the adaptation to an arid environment. An attempt was made to develop a methodology which would be useful in
other areas. Bennett's cultural ecology field work project in Southwestern
Saskatchewan is concerned with adaptive behavior under economic conditions
of high risk and uncertainty due to weather.[1] It could be spoken of as a
study of socioeconomic and cultural change from the standpoint of adaptation
to the environment. According to Bennett, innovative capacity and adaptive
economic arrangements are themselves established or very importantly influenced by the social arrangements.

Perception in Resource Management

The field of natural resources is one in which the concept of perception has many useful applications. This has been clearly recognized and has
been integrated into two different theoretical frameworks for analyzing decisions in resource use.[2] Firey, a sociologist, suggests that there are three
distinct frames of reference for explaining resource phenomena. These are
the ecological, focusing on what is physically possible, the ethnological,
concerned with what is perceived to be adoptable, and the economic, which
considers what would be profitable. The ethnological approach shows an appreciation of the role of cultural differences in perception of possible resource uses. An awareness of the importance of individual perception is
evident in the framework employed by the geographer, White. He uses the
term theoretical range of choice to refer to all the adjustments and uses
practiced in similar environments in the past plus possible innovations.
Then he shows that a more limited practical range of choice may result due
to various restraints or a lack of awareness on the part of the resource
manager.

In recent years there has been an increasing amount of work by
geographers utilizing the concept of perception in natural resource studies.
The diversity within this group is suggestive of the wide range of applications for this type of work. Lucas delimited wilderness areas within a wider
park area according to people's perceptions.[3] He suggested that variations

---

[1]Bennett, _Plains Anthropologist_, VII, 86-90.

[2]Walter Firey, _Man, Mind and Land: A Theory of Resource Use_
(Glencoe, Free Press, 1960), 256pp., and Gilbert F. White, "The Choice
of Use in Resource Management," _Natural Resources Journal_, I (1961), 23-40.

[3]Robert Lucas, "Wilderness Perception and Use: The Example of the
Boundary Waters Canoe Area," _Natural Resources Journal_, III, No. 3 (1963),
394-411.

in wilderness perception between such different users as canoeists and motor
boaters may provide guidelines for future zoning of areas for different uses.
Blaut and others investigated the reasons why conservation methods were not
being accepted by farmers in the severely eroded Blue Mountains of Jamaica.
Among the reasons he found was the fact that the farmers fail entirely to
perceive or perceive imperfectly the process of soil erosion in cause and
effect terms.

A very different study but one which underlines the importance of taking
into consideration the resource managers' perception of the situation was concerned with stock reduction on the Navaho tribal range.[2] Fonaroff demonstrated
the negative aspects of a lack of concern for the resource managers' perception. He described the difficulties which arose when the government tried
to reorient the whole technological basis of Navaho society without adequately
understanding how the recommended practices would be affected by these
people's attitudes toward nature and their understanding of the reasons for
the changes. Similarly, any attempts to change the behavior of the Great
Plains farmer at the start of the chapter would probably be unsuccessful
if they failed to take into consideration his positive perception of environmental possibilities.

Gould[3] and Wolpert,[4] in two separate studies, show a similarity in
their use of perception as a variable in resource use. Using different types
of models and examining the deviations from the pattern based on the model's
assumptions they are able to focus on the difference between optimal and
actual use, and how this is influenced by the perception of the resource
managers.

Variations in criteria for scenic beauty were investigated by Lowenthal[5]

[1]J. Blaut et al., "A Study of Cultural Determinants of Soil Erosion
and Conservation in the Blue Mountains of Jamaica," Social and Economic
Studies, VIII (1959), 402-420.

[2]L. Schuyler Fonaroff, "Conservation and Stock Reduction on the Navaho
Tribal Range," Geographical Review, LIII (1963), 200-223.

[3]Peter R. Gould, "Man Against His Environment: A Game Theoretic Framework," Annals of the Association of American Geographers, LIII (1963), 290-
297.

[4]Julian Wolpert, "The Decision Process in Spatial Context," Annals of
the Association of American Geographers, LIV, No.4 (1964), 537-538.

[5]David Lowenthal, "Not Every Prospect Pleases," Landscape (Winter,
1962), pp. 19-23.

who later in collaboration with Prince[1] showed the effect on the English
landscape of those criteria chosen by Englishmen in the past.

Porter has done a considerable amount of work investigating the way
certain groups of people in East Africa perceive their natural environment.[2]
He found, for example, that the Pokot people in Kenya had a discriminating
perception of the functional differences in soil types and altitudinal zones
of their environment. They did not use the same criteria as a Western sci-
entist might but they had an internally consistent scheme which is meaningful
in Pokot life. More directly pertinent to the present study are Porter's investigations of Pokot and Wakamba adjustments to various environmental zones.[3]
Where the environmental gradient was extremely steep so as to provide clearly
different types of areas there was usually an explicit and successful adaptation to each and even specialized reciprocal economies. But where there was
a gradual transition between dissimilar zones maladjustments were found. In
the middle ranges where nature is ambiguous and the agricultural limits are
not clear the people had not yet found a workable solution. These findings
have clear parallels with those of the flood plain studies discussed below
and with a similar assessment of degrees of adjustment in different zones
within the Great Plains which is attempted in chapter vi.

Perception of Natural Hazards

The immediate forerunner of the present study and the single strongest organized research tradition leading toward perception studies in natural
resources is the series of flood plain studies at the University of Chicago
and their derivatives. The theme of these studies is directly relevant to
the investigation of perception of the drought hazard for it seems likely
that the way in which people deal with the natural catastrophe of floods
may be similar to their behavior vis-à-vis droughts.

The first of these flood plain studies was White's general typology

---

[1]David Lowenthal and Hugh C. Prince, "The English Landscape,"
Geographical Review, LIV, No. 3 (1964), 309-346. See also, David Lowenthal
and Hugh C. Prince, "English Landscape Tastes," Geographical Review, LV,
No. 2 (1965), 186-222.

[2]Philip W. Porter, "Pokot Ideas Concerning Soil," a chapter on
Pokot. (Mimeographed.) See also by the same author, "Suk Views on Suk
Environments," Paper read at meetings of the American Association of
Geographers, Denver, Colorado, September 1-5, 1963.

[3]Philip W. Porter, "Environmental Potentials and Economic Opportun-
ities--A Background for Cultural Adaptation," American Anthropologist,
LXVII, No. 2 (1965), 409-420.

of human adjustments to floods.[1] At this early stage the main emphasis was on physical factors affecting such adjustments. Later studies turned more and more toward an assessment of social, economic, and behavioral variables and the ways in which these interacted to produce the observable patterns of flood plain occupance in rural and urban areas.[2] Attitude studies followed which revealed no associations between attitudes toward future flooding and socioeconomic class or knowledge of protection structures.[3]

The two most recent studies in the series are the companion volumes of Kates and White.[4] Kates concentrated more directly on the perception of the flood hazard and of the range of choice as related to the decision-making process, while White examined the circumstances in which private and public managers choose among several possible adjustments to floods. Both found experience to be a strong factor in the perception of resource managers. The flood plain dwellers' perception of the flood hazard was strongly affected by what Kates for emphasis calls "the prison of experience." White also found a strong association between those who perceive or adopt structural measures and their length of tenure in the flood plain, and between the perception or adoption of emergency measures and their location within the reach of the latest major flood.

Some derivatives of the flood plain research tradition have tended to focus more directly on the perception of resource managers while broadening out to consider a wider range of natural hazards. Thus Burton and Kates compare the flood plain and the seashore and perception of the hazards of each by the respective groups of inhabitants.[5] They found that managers of coastal

---

[1]Gilbert F. White, Human Adjustment to Floods, Department of Geography Research Paper No. 29, University of Chicago (Chicago: Department of Geography, 1945).

[2]Ian Burton, Types of Agricultural Occupance of Flood Plains in the United States, Department of Geography Research Paper No. 75, University of Chicago (Chicago: By the author, 1962); Gilbert F. White (ed.), Changes in the Urban Occupance of Flood Plains in the United States, Department of Geography Research Paper No. 57, University of Chicago (Chicago: Department of Geography, 1961).

[3]Wolf Roder, "Attitude and Knowledge on the Topeka Flood Plain"; Ian Burton, "Invasion and Escape on the Little Calumet," Papers on Flood Problems, ed. Gilbert F. White, Department of Geography Research Paper No. 70 University of Chicago (Chicago: 1960).

[4]Robert W. Kates, Hazard and Choice Perception in Flood Plain Management, Department of Geography Research Paper No. 78, University of Chicago (Chicago: By the author, 1962); Gilbert F. White, Choice of Adjustment to Floods, Department of Geography Research Paper No. 93, University of Chicago (Chicago: Department of Geography, 1964).

[5]Ian Burton and Robert W. Kates, "The Floodplain and the Seashore," Geographical Review, LIV, No. 3 (1964), 366-385; see also, Ian Burton,

properties had a greater awareness of the hazards of storms than did urban flood plain dwellers. But though aware of the hazard, the coastal dwellers tended to underestimate the frequency, likelihood or probability of storm damage. The entire range of natural hazards is analyzed by the same two authors.[1] They discuss the definition, classification, magnitude and frequency of natural hazards, and variations in perception of them and advance three explanatory factors for variations in the perception of natural hazards among users of the same resource.[2] The first depends on the relation of the hazard to the dominant resource use, with heightened hazard perception expected where the hazard is directly related to the resource use. The second is that frequency of natural events is related to the perception of the hazard. The third states that perception varies with the degree of personal experience. They found that social class and education were not significantly associated with perception of hazards. If these factors hold true over the entire range of natural hazards, one might expect Great Plains wheat farmers to have heightened hazard perception since the success of their livelihood is directly related to the drought hazard. Similarly, there should be variations in drought perception from area to area due to areal differences in the frequency of drought occurrence. Furthermore, there should be variations in drought perception resulting from differences in the amount of personal experience of the individual farmers. These possibilities will be investigated in the chapters which follow.

Suggested Lines for Further Research

Generalizing from the above discussion of perception in geography one could suggest that there are two broad groups of questions for which answers are being sought. The first has to do with the effect of the impersonal environment on individuals and groups. It is not clear what the

---

Robert W. Kates, John R. Mather and Rodman E. Snead, The Shores of Megalopolis: Coastal Occupance and Human Adjustment to Flood Hazard (Publications in Climatology, XVIII, No. 3 [1965], 435-603; Elmer, N.J.: C. W. Thornthwaite Associates Laboratory of Climatology).

[1]Ian Burton and Robert W. Kates, "The Perception of Natural Hazards in Resource Management," Natural Resources Journal, III, No. 3 (1964), 412-441. This issue of the Natural Resources Journal contains papers resulting from a symposium on "Perception and Natural Resources" which includes separate papers by Lucas and by Quinney in addition to the one by Burton and Kates.

[2]Ibid., p. 426.

effective stimulus dimensions of the natural environment are.[1] Nor is it known what effects, if any, they have on human motivation, social institutions, personality structure, national character, rural-urban differences, and adaptation to new environments. The second series of questions is concerned with the way in which people perceive the physical world, how their experience structures their perception, and how this affects their behavior.[2] Much more information is needed on how people perceive their own environment and the rest of the world.[3] What is noticed and responded to and how is this conditioned by language and culture? At what ages and stages are ideas about the physical world acquired and what are the educational implications of this?[4]

The hard conditions of the Great Plains provide a severe testing ground for man-environment hypotheses. The environmental stimulation is much more stressful than most places so that the relationship between it and perception, between perception and adaptation or between environmental stress and personality characteristics can be more directly approached here. The study areas, samples and methods chosen, and the rationale for their choice is outlined in the chapter which follows.

---

[1] An attempt by a psychologist to pull together important factors in the human environment which would probably be useful for anyone working on such a problem is Isidor Chein, "The Environment as a Determinant of Behavior," The Journal of Social Psychology, XXXIX (1954), 115-127.

[2] One variation of this type is "what are the limits of their world?" This was examined by D. Whittlesey, "Horizon of Geography," Annals of the Association of American Geographers, XXXV (1945), 1-36.

[3] The rest of the world may be perceived in terms of a series of stereotypes by many people. See John Haddon, "A View of Foreign Lands," Geography, LXV (1960), 286-289. A thoughtful discussion of studies of personality in relation to nationality, national stereotypes, attitudes and their modification is contained in the broadly ranging survey by Otto Klineberg, Tensions Affecting International Understanding, A Survey of Research (New York: Social Science Research Council Bulletin 60, 1950).

[4] A test was developed to compare geographic concepts acquired by Japanese and American high school students by Setsuko Mitsuhashi, "Geographic Concepts of High School Students" (unpublished Master's dissertation, Department of Geography, University of Chicago, 1962).

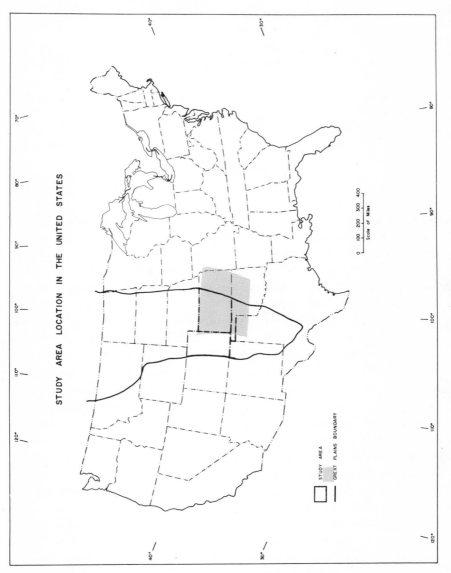

STUDY AREA LOCATION IN THE UNITED STATES

STUDY AREA

GREAT PLAINS BOUNDARY

Scale of Miles

0 100 200 300 400

Fig. 2

CHAPTER III

STUDY AREAS, SAMPLE, AND METHOD

Oh this guy here was walking out across his land. Things are looking pretty tough. Dirt is blowing. He's wondering whether it's worth
it all or not. Them were the days when he wondered whether to keep on
struggling or try something else.

Choice of Study Areas

To test the hypotheses a series of six areas was selected within the
winter wheat belt of the Central Great Plains (see Figure 2 for location of
the study area). The selection was made so as to include areas which dif-
fered along the dimensions to be tested and which reflected some of the
broader regional differences within the Central Great Plains.

Several possible indices of drought hazard were considered and rejected. Federal Crop Insurance statistics were examined for possible use
as an index of the risk. However, since some of the most droughty areas are
not covered and since percentage coverage varies considerably from county to
county, this plan was abandoned. Similarly, an examination was made of areas
which had been declared drought emergency areas during the period 1950-1965.
There seems little doubt that drought emergency areas are those experiencing
severe or extreme drought according to the Palmer Index and usually there have
been a couple of years of drought prior to the time they are so designated.
However, as an objective measure they fail because all areas with similar
meteorological drought conditions are not necessarily included. In addition
drought emergency areas seem to follow state lines much more closely than
one expects natural conditions to do. Figure 3 showing the number of times
each county in the Central Great Plains was declared a drought emergency
area illustrates some of the strange patterns which are found. Cimarron
County, Oklahoma, and Finney County, Kansas, both suffered approximately
equal amounts of severe and extreme drought during the period in question.
But, for some reason, possibly the larger amounts of feed available in

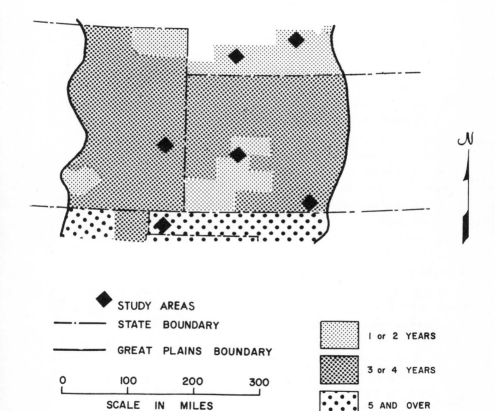

TOTAL NUMBER OF YEARS DECLARED DROUGHT
EMERGENCY AREAS 1952 - 1964

◆ STUDY AREAS

—·— STATE BOUNDARY

——— GREAT PLAINS BOUNDARY

0   100   200   300
SCALE   IN   MILES

1 or 2 YEARS

3 or 4 YEARS

5 AND OVER

SOURCE : U.S.D.A. AGRICULTURAL STABILIZATION AND
CONSERVATION SERVICE

Fig. 3

irrigated Western Kansas, there was a great difference in the number of times each was declared a drought emergency area (see Figure 4 for individual years declared drought emergency areas).

The Thornthwaite moisture index was chosen as the best easily obtainable objective measure of aridity.[1] Plotted on a map, the pattern resembles that of the natural vegetation zones as delimited by Shantz.[2] Within each of the three major vegetation zones two counties were chosen so that differences within the zones could be compared as well as differences between zones. The counties finally chosen are listed in Table 5 according to the degree of aridity as measured by the Thornthwaite moisture index (see Figure 5 for locations). The number interviewed in each area is shown.

TABLE 5

STUDY AREAS AND SIZE OF SAMPLE

County	State	County Seat	No. Interviewed	Degree of Aridity (TMI)
Adams	Nebraska	Hastings	17	- 9.24
Barber	Kansas	Medicine Lodge	16	-16.20
Frontier	Nebraska	Curtis	15	-19.16
Finney	Kansas	Garden City	17	-24.44
Cimarron	Oklahoma	Boise City	14	-27.25
Kiowa	Colorado	Eads	17 / 96	-31.39

Within each county a smaller area was chosen for detailed study after consultation with the county agent, and officials in the local Soil Conservation Service and Agricultural Stabilization and Conservation Service offices (henceforth SCS and ASC). An effort was made to select a township or other small community area which was fairly representative of the county in terms

---

[1] The moisture regions obtained by plotting the Thornthwaite moisture index on a map of the United States can be seen in Thornthwaite, Geographical Review, XXXVII, No. 1, 55-94. A somewhat smaller version is found in Goode's World Atlas, ed. Edward B. Espenshade, Jr. (12th edition; Chicago: Rand, McNally & Co., 1965), p. 53.

[2] See H. L. Shantz, "The Natural Vegetation of the Great Plains Region," Annals of the Association of American Geographers, XIII (1923), 83. A more recent vegetation map with an accompanying manual is that of A. W. Küchler, Potential Natural Vegetation of the Coterminous United States (Special Publication No. 36; New York: American Geographical Society, 1964).

DECLARED DROUGHT EMERGENCY AREAS

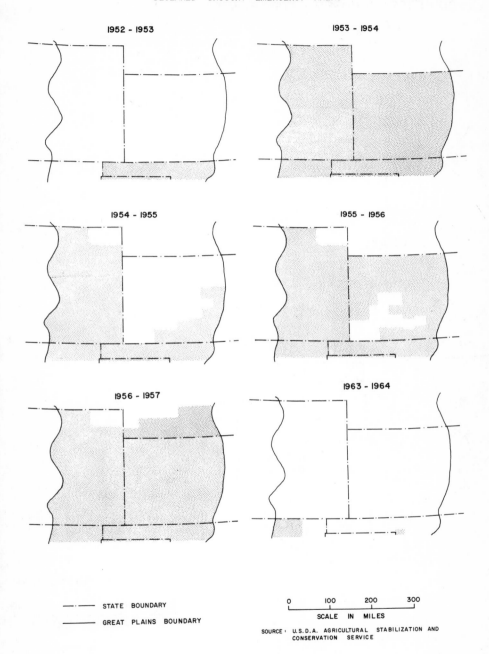

1952 - 1953

1953 - 1954

1954 - 1955

1955 - 1956

1956 - 1957

1963 - 1964

—·—·— STATE BOUNDARY

———— GREAT PLAINS BOUNDARY

0   100   200   300
SCALE   IN   MILES

SOURCE· U.S.D.A. AGRICULTURAL   STABILIZATION AND
CONSERVATION   SERVICE

Fig. 4

COUNTIES CHOSEN FOR SAMPLES

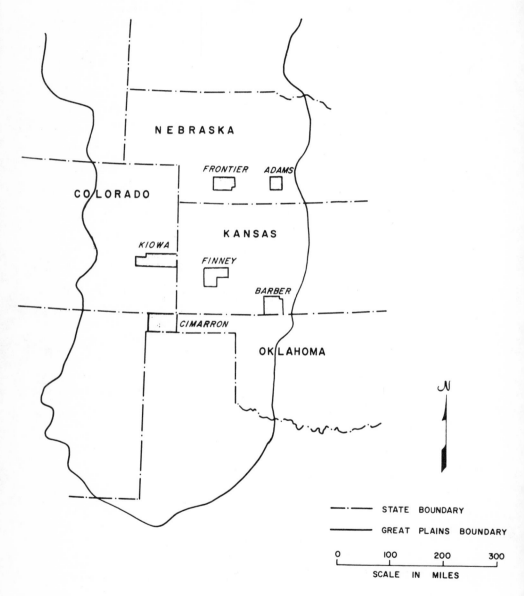

Fig. 5

of such factors as size of farms, type of operation, and quality of land, farmers, and farming practices. A more restricted area than the county was chosen to minimize soil differences and variations in rainfall amounts due to local showers. It also tended to maximize convenience in interviewing. The areas were chosen as close to the local weather station as possible since these data would be used for comparison with the farmers' responses.

Within each township or community area selected a random sample of farmers was taken from the wheat allotment records of the local ASC office. Table 6 shows the community areas chosen and the percentage of all farmers within the area that were included in the sample. With the help of local

TABLE 6

COMMUNITY AREAS CHOSEN

County	Township or Community Area	Per Cent of All Farmers Interviewed
Adams	Juniata Township	16
Barber	Nippawalla Community	58
Frontier	Sheridan Precinct	88
Finney	Pierceville Community (Portions North of the Arkansas River)	33
Cimarron	Garlington Neighborhood (Township No. 3-6)	30
Kiowa	Eads Community	22

officials a few clearly inappropriate persons were culled out. These included such categories as sick or absent persons, retired persons who work a few acres, high school students who do likewise, and part-time farmers with very small acreages. Letters were then sent out by the county agent to those in the final sample. They warned the farmer that an interviewer was coming but assured him that the information would be kept strictly confidential and would be used for scientific rather than commercial purposes. The goal in each area was approximately seventeen farmers to make up a grand total of 100 for all six areas.[1]

---

[1] The great mobility of some of the Great Plains farmers is illustrated by the reason why only 96 rather than 100 farmers were interviewed. In Cimarron County, Oklahoma, where interviews took place early in December, three of the farmers drawn in the sample, having completed the fall seeding, had left the area. Two were wintering elsewhere, one in Aguascalientes, Mexico, another at Taos, New Mexico; while the third was off in another

Description of Areas

Table 7 describes the chief dimensions of the counties chosen. All
had several characteristics in common. In topography, according to Hammond's
map,[1] all were plains areas, four being smooth plains and two irregular
plains. In all cases the local relief was within 100 to 300 feet mainly
concentrated in valleys while the uplands were gently sloping. The farmers
in all areas averaged between ten and twelve years of schooling completed.
In general the more humid and northern areas had been settled the longest
as indicated by the number of years the farmers' families had been in the
area. In all cases the average age of the farmers interviewed was over
forty years and the average number of years of farming experience in the area
was over twenty years. Winter wheat is a main crop in all six areas.[2]

Two Dry Areas

Adams County, Nebraska, and Barber County, Kansas, were chosen as
examples of areas close to the humid margin of the Great Plains. Both have
an annual precipitation of over 24 inches but this amount is more effective
in the former because of the somewhat cooler temperatures. This is reflected
in the Thornthwaite moisture index which is -9.24 for Hastings, Nebraska, and
-16.20 for Medicine Lodge, Kansas, the respective county seats. This is a
considerable difference in aridity but both stations fall within the eastern-
most of the three vegetation zones as outlined by Shantz.

In terms of population and communication characteristics Adams County
is a "sutland" area while Barber County is a "yonland" area. The population
density for the former is 52 persons per square mile and only eight per square

---

state visiting folks for an undetermined amount of time. In Barber County,
Kansas, one of the sample farmers was in the hospital when the interviewer
arrived.

[1]Edwin H. Hammond, "Classes of Land-Surface Form in the Forty Eight
States," Map Supplement No. 4 (Washington, D.C.: Association of American
Geographers, 1963). See also the discussion on the preparation of the map
in Edwin H. Hammond,"Analysis of Properties in Land Form Geography: An Ap-
plication to Broad-Scale Land Form Mapping," Annals of the Association of
American Geographers, LIV, No. 1 (1964), 11-19.

[2]To see how closely the study area corresponds to area of winter
wheat, see William Van Royen, The Agricultural Resources of the World (Vol. I,
Atlas of the World's Resources; New York: Prentice-Hall, 1954), fig. 36,
p. 32. See also, the map "Major Land Uses in the United States" (Washington:
U. S. Department of Agriculture, Bureau of Agricultural Economics, 1950).

TABLE 7

CHIEF CHARACTERISTICS OF COUNTIES CHOSEN

County & State	Average Annual ppt. (in in.)	Thorn-thwaite Moisture Index	Vegetation (Shantz)	Vegetation (Küchler)	Topography (Hammond)	Population Density per Sq. Mile	Average Size of Farm (Acres)	No. of Years in Area		Av. Age	Av. Ed.
								Farmer	Family		
Adams Nebraska	24.28	- 9.24	Needle Grass and slender wheatgrass	Bluestem prairie	Smooth plains 50-75% of gentle slope on upland	52	320.6	23.9	73.6	46.8	10.1
Barber Kansas	24.50	-16.20	Bluestem bunch grass	Bluestem grama prairie	Irregular plain 50-75% of gentle slope on upland	8	1157.5	26.2	51.0	52.5	11.2
Frontier Nebraska	19.13	-19.16	Wiregrass	Wheat grass bluestem needle grass	Irregular plain 50-75% of gentle slope on upland	5	1375.3	21.6	62.4	42.2	11.2
Finney Kansas	18.67	-24.44	Wiregrass	Grama Buffalo grass	Smooth plains 50-75% of gentle slope on upland	12	1432.1	24.2	36.5	49.7	10.6
Cimarron Oklahoma	16.51	-27.25	Grama & Buffalo grass	Grama Buffalo grass	Smooth plains 50-75% of gentle slope on upland	3	1960.4	22.7	41.1	44.0	11.7
Kiowa Colorado	13.64	-31.39	Grama & Buffalo grass	Grama Buffalo grass	Smooth plains 50-75% of gentle slope on upland	1	4289.9	21.0	32.9	47.5	10.5

mile for the latter. Hastings, Nebraska, has a much larger population and
range of services than Medicine Lodge, Kansas. The roads in Juniata Township
are mainly hard-surface all-weather roads while those in Kansas county area
are unfinished dirt roads which are incredibly bad in wet weather. The average age and amount of experience is somewhat higher for the Barber County
sample while Adams County has been settled for the longest period of time.

     The two areas also differ somewhat in topography and type of opera-
tion. The area in Barber County is somewhat rougher, the farms considerably
larger in acreage and there is more emphasis on livestock, mainly cattle.
The area in Adams County is in the corn belt transition zone with larger
total yields of corn and sorghum than wheat. Over half of the sample from
Adams County use some irrigation as opposed to none in the Barber County
group.

Two Drier Areas

     Frontier County, Nebraska and Finney County, Kansas were selected as
samples near the center of the Great Plains. Both fall within the second of
the broad vegetation zones described by Shantz as wiregrass. The average annual precipitation at the county seats are 19.13 for Curtis and 18.67 inches
for Garden City. The Thornthwaite Moisture Index indicates more arid conditions near Garden City (-24.44) than at Curtis (-19.16). This increased
aridity shows up in Küchler's map of vegetation which places the Finney County
location just within the grama buffalo grass zone while the other area is
placed in the wheat grass, blue stem, needle-grass category. The average size
of farms is very close, 1,375 acres for the Frontier County sample and 1,432
acres for the Finney County sample. Among the latter group almost half irrigate to some degree while the other group contains only two irrigators.

     There are a number of differences between the two areas. In the very
flat Finney County area cash grain is by far the most common type of operation. Frontier County with many deep ravines and canyon-like topography has
more diversified operations with greater emphasis on livestock. The population density is 12 per square mile in Finney County while Frontier County has
only 5 per square mile. Garden City provides a large portion of Southwestern
Kansas with a wide range of services. It is located on major east-west and
north-south highways. Many of those in the Finney County sample were sidewalk
farmers residing in Garden City. Curtis, Nebraska, is much smaller, more iso-
lated from major highways and in the study area dirt roads were the rule.
Thus the Finney County area would be classified as sutland while the Frontier
County precinct would be considered yonland. The average age of the Frontier

County sample was seven years less than their Finney County equivalents though
there was less of a gap in years of farming experience.

The Two Driest Areas

The two driest study areas are located on the most arid edges of
Great Plains cropland. Boise City in Cimarron County, Oklahoma, has an average
annual precipitation of 16.51 inches and a Thornthwaite Moisture Index of
-27.25. The Eads Community of Kiowa County, Colorado, is even more arid.[1]
The average annual precipitation at Eads is 13.64 inches while the Thornthwaite Moisture Index is -31.39. Both are extremely flat and sparsely
populated. In Kiowa County there are wide expanses of grassland. In fact,
most of the original sod was intact until the 1940s. This is reflected in
the fact that the Kiowa County sample's average number of years of experience
is lowest of the six areas though the average age of farmers is third highest. The average number of years the family had been in the area was also
lowest for Kiowa County where many of those interviewed represented the first
generation in the region.

The population density is three persons per square mile in Cimarron
County, Oklahoma, and one person per square mile in Kiowa County, Colorado.
In both areas there were a substantial number of sidewalk farmers in the
sample. In Kiowa County several suitcase farmers were drawn as well. The
average acreage among the Colorado sample was 4,290 acres,[2] considerably
larger than the 1960 acre average for the Cimarron County group. Both would
be considered yonland in terms of population density, and in the lack of
local radio stations and daily newspaper services; but the Boise City area
has somewhat better roads, a larger population and perhaps a larger range
of services than the Eads Community.

The Interview

All interviews were conducted by the writer who visited the farmers
at their homes. The interview consisted of two parts, first the questionnaire, and second the modified version of the Thematic Apperception Test

---

[1]For a detailed discussion of recommended practices and managerial
strategies for Kiowa County, see Kiowa County Agricultural Advisory Council,
"Farm and Ranch Guide for Kiowa County" (Colorado State Agricultural Extension Service Headbook; Fort Collins: Colorado State University Extension
Service, August, 1958), 50pp.

[2]The average size of farm in the Kiowa County sample is estimated to
be about 50 per cent higher than the county average. Letter from Mr. Bruce G.
Whitmore, Extension Agent, Kiowa County, February 10, 1966.

(henceforth TAT). Total time for both was approximately one hour. The questionnaire was given first with the interviewer asking all the questions and marking the responses. The farmer at no time saw the questionnaire directly so there was no possibility of him gaining an idea as to what the anticipated categories for any question were. An effort was made at all times to record spontaneous comments and questions as they appeared. After the questionnaire was completed and rapport established the farmers were given the standard TAT instructions and they told stories about each of the pictures presented. The interviewer recorded these by hand as they were being told. In general the farmers were cooperative with perhaps one from each area showing a certain reluctance to submit to the ordeal. However, all answered the questionnaire and only two of the total ninety-six contacted refused to tell stories about the pictures.

The Questionnaire

The first series of questions in the questionnaire were concerned with general background information such as age of farmer, education, number of years in area, type of operation, and income (see appendix ii). The next major section was concerned with the farmers' perception of the drought hazard. They were asked about past, present and future droughts, how often expected and how defined. Included were questions regarding the range of choice perceived by the farmer, both in type of operation and in kinds of practices seen as effective in minimizing the drought risk. Following this came a section on various types of farming practices such as stubble mulch, strip cropping, and use of fertilizers; and the use of certain strategies such as reserves or credit. The emphasis was on how the farmer perceived them, whether or not he had adopted them, why he thought he had or hadn't and when. By means of a self-rating scale and information as to the time of adoption of various practices it was possible to classify the farmers according to adopter categories. This was further checked for accuracy against the ratings of the county agents for each farmer. Another group of questions was designed to find the attitudes of the farmers toward water witching, weather modification, and luck as a factor in farming success.

The Thematic Apperception Test

Murray's Thematic Apperception Test was used.[1] Six of the standard Murray cards were used plus four extra ones designed to probe attitudes

---

[1] Henry A. Murray, Thematic Apperception Test: Pictures and Manual (Cambridge: Harvard University Press, 1943).

toward drought, weather and farmer peer group relationships (see Figures 6 to 9 for extra pictures used).[1]

   The procedure is merely that of presenting a series of pictures to a subject and encouraging him to tell stories about them, invented on the spur of the moment. The fact that stories collected in this way often reveal significant components of personality is dependent on the prevalence of two psychological tendencies: the tendency of people to interpret an ambiguous human situation in conformity with their past experiences and present wants, and the tendency of those who write stories to do likewise: draw on the fund of their experiences and express their sentiments and needs, whether conscious or unconscious.[2]

   For the purpose of this study only two of the ten pictures were analyzed in a thorough fashion but others were used to gain indications of certain traits such as attitude toward nature. Of the two cards analyzed in a thorough fashion one was the standard Murray card number one. It is a picture in which a young boy is contemplating a violin which rests on a table in front of him. The personality areas generally revealed by responses to this picture are concerned with how people handle the issue of achievement.[3] The kind of story told will provide indications of the relationship between personal needs and the demands of cultural agents, in the area of achievement. The second card used was that illustrated in Figure 6. It is a picture taken for the United States Department of Agriculture entitled "Dust Over the Dakotas." It shows a lone figure bending into the wind as dust swirls around. It represents extreme drought conditions which are the occasional experience of all Great Plains farmers. It is thus appropriate in combination with Murray Card 1, as it reveals an actual situation the farmer is likely to face, and one which is likely to affect his chances of achievement.

   The Schaw-Henry technique was used in interpreting the stories.[4] This is a technique developed for the study of non-clinical groups. From each story is abstracted the story-core or dominant theme. This theme has three parts, the initial phase which sets the stage, the manipulatory stage in which the action takes place, and the resolution or outcome. The ter-

---

[1]Some of the general principles for selection of pictures for special purposes are outlined in P. M. Symonds, "Criteria for the Selection of Pictures for the Investigation of Adolescent Fantasies," Journal of Abnormal and Social Psychology, XXXIV (1939), 271-274.

[2]Murray, p. 1.

[3]William E. Henry, The Analysis of Fantasy: The Thematic Apperception Technique in the Study of Personality (New York: John Wiley and Sons, Inc., 1956), p. 240.

[4]Louis C. Schaw and William E. Henry, "A Method for the Comparison of Groups: A Study in Thematic Apperception," Genetic Psychology Monographs, LIV (1956), 207-253.

Fig. 6.--Card A.
(Source: U. S. D. A. Photo)

Fig. 7.--Card **B**.
(Source: U. S. D. A. Photo)

Fig. 8.--Card C.
(Source: Bob Taylor, Cordell, Oklahoma)

Fig. 9.--Card D.

(Source: Dept. of Information, College of Agriculture and Home Economics, University of Nebraska

minology used in abstracting the themes is Murray's need-press scheme.[1]
After each person's story to a particular picture has been analyzed the
themes are classified and the groups can be compared on the basis of the
frequency of various themes, and the kinds of actions and resolutions found
within each type of story. The following is an example of how a thema is abstracted from a story.

> This is a boy and his violin. He is looking at it and thinking he
> would like to become a violinist. So he picks up the violin and trys
> to play. His parents are pleased and encourage him in his ambition to
> become a violinist. So he practices regularly and follows his teacher's
> instructions faithfully and eventually becomes a concert violinist.

The issue of the story can be stated as follows: a boy, desirous of becoming a violinist (need Achievement: nAch), is encouraged by his parents (fused
press NurturanceAchievement: fpNurAch), and applies himself vigorously to the
task of learning how to play the violin (need Work: nWk). This leads to success (Achievement: Ach) and a good outcome (GO). In abstract need-press terms
the theme of the story is:

Basic Stem	Coping Mechanism	Resolution	Outcome
nAch	fpNurAch; nWk	Ach	GO

The aim is abstraction of the story's meaning rather than analysis of the
individual storyteller's psychodynamics. Since the theoretically possible
range of stories is infinite much of the idiosyncratic richness must be lost
in attempting group comparisons. The principal task in utilizing a group
method of analysis is to abstract to the degree that maximally preserves that
which makes one story different from another without precluding group analysis.[2] This type of analysis reduces the clinical judgment involved but there
still remains a certain interpretive element.[3] Since the analyst's judgment
is involved in every step of the process the question of reliability of that
judgment is of great importance.[4]

---

[1] For a complete description of the terminology see, Henry A. Murray,
Explorations in Personality (New York: Science Editions, 1962), chap. iv.
This book was originally published by Oxford University Press in 1930.

[2] For a more thorough description of the problems involved, from which
this discussion was abstracted, see John N. Sims, "Psychodynamics of Two
Levels of Executives in the Federal Civil Service" (unpublished Ph.D. dissertation, Committee on Human Development, University of Chicago, 1964), pp.
31-35.

[3] For a review of the literature which discusses some attempts to use
projective tests for comparison of groups of various types, see Gardner
Lindzey, Projective Techniques and Cross-Cultural Research (New York: Appleton-Century-Crofts, 1961).

[4] The writer's work benefited by the close supervision of Mr. John
Sims under whose guidance the method was learned and with whom the various
categories were compared after individual interpretation.

The Palmer Drought Index

For each area the Palmer Drought Index was obtained for each month from 1924 to the date of the interview. This is the time period for which complete climatic data were available for all six areas. It also includes the time period during which almost all of the present farmers obtained their experience. Just under 10 per cent of the farmers in the sample were already farming at an earlier date. In all cases but two the drought index was worked out for the weather data at the county seat. The exceptions were Frontier County, Nebraska, and Cimarron County, Oklahoma. For the former, data from Curtis were used rather than Stockville, the county seat. Curtis is the principal town in the county, the weather station is there, and the study area was chosen as close to it as possible. In Cimarron County complete data were not available for Boise City. In this case data for Kenton, Oklahoma, were used. Kenton is approximately 30 miles west of Boise City as the crow flies but there appears to be a fairly steep gradient in climatic conditions here so that the index here is not quite as representative as the others.

The objective drought record as revealed by the Palmer Index was compared with the responses of the farmers to investigate the accuracy of their perception of various aspects of the drought hazard.

Other Data Obtained

In each of the study areas the county agents were asked to look over the list of practices and strategies and to make an assessment as to which were most applicable in their area. This serves as another check on the farmers' perception of the same thing.

One other set of data was gathered in three of the areas. Three junior high school classes, one each in Eads, Colorado, Boise City, Oklahoma, and Medicine Lodge, Kansas, were given Beck's Spatial Symbols Test.[1] It was hypothesized that distinctive preferences in terms of personal spatial styles would differentiate Plains people from people raised in other environments.

Limitations of the Study Design

The researcher's conflict in deciding which areas to choose is analogous to that of the wheat farmer, at the start of the chapter, who must decide how

---

[1] Robert J. Beck, "A Comparative Study of Spatial Meaning" (unpublished Master's thesis, Committee on Human Development, University of Chicago, 1964).

to handle drought. If the three sets of two areas had been more carefully matched in terms of topography, type of operation and moisture index, there may have been a firmer basis for making certain kinds of statements. As it is, the slight differences in topography lead to somewhat different needs in terms of conservation practices such as terracing and to differences in type of operation. The differences due to type of operation may tend to obscure somewhat such relationships as those between perception and aridity or perception and experience since the effect of the aridity or the quality of the experience would differ under these different circumstances. To accurately assess the relative degree of adjustment of different areas a more complete list of practices would have helped as well as a more careful comparison of the way practices were applied since there appear to be variations. The moisture index varied considerably between pairs so that only rough comparisons can be made. In spite of this limitation, many interesting relationships appear to be strong enough to show through. These will be discussed in the chapters which follow.

CHAPTER IV

PERCEPTION OF THE DROUGHT HAZARD

. . . This is a picture taken from the drought days out west. It's
pretty desolate and bare and you can tell by the buildings it hasn't
been too prosperous for 'em. I would say they've been right in the middle of a drought. The younger boy is not crying but has his hand in
front of his face. The man and the older boy they're going to get in
out of it anyway. He's going to tell those boys when they get in there,
"Well we didn't raise any crops this year but wait 'til next year."
Because that is the biggest next year country in the world out there.

Awareness of the Drought Hazard

Preliminary reconnaisance work quickly established the fact that
Great Plains wheat farmers speak frequently, animatedly, and in dry spells,
almost exclusively about drought.[1] Before probing more fully the various
aspects of drought perception each farmer was asked the general question,
"What are the main advantages and disadvantages of this area?" Although
they were not then aware that the main purpose of the interview was to examine the question of drought, eighty-one of the ninety-six interviewed
(84 per cent) mentioned dryness or lack of moisture as a disadvantage.
Usually it was the first, most emphatic, and often the only disadvantage
mentioned. Table 8 shows the percentage in each area who mentioned dryness
as a disadvantage.

Perception of present moisture conditions was also clear. However,
there appears to be a tendency to judge present moisture conditions not
only according to long term averages but also in terms of the immediately
preceding conditions. Table 9 shows the farmers' answers to the question,

---

[1]This became apparent during the several week period of preliminary
reconnaisance work and pretesting during the summer of 1964. An example of
a similar comment made in reference to Northwestern Oklahoma is "Rain, the
lack of it, or the possibility of it enters into nearly every person's daily
thoughts and forms a topic of discussion and conversation" from B. A. Botkin
(ed.), A Treasury of Western Folklore (New York: Crown Publishers Inc.,
1951), p. 85.

TABLE 8

PERCENTAGE OF FARMERS MENTIONING DRYNESS AS A DISADVANTAGE

County	Adams	Barber	Frontier	Finney	Cimmaron	Kiowa
%	71	87	67	94	86	100

TABLE 9

FARMERS' ASSESSMENT OF PRESENT MOISTURE CONDITIONS

County	Adams	Barber	Frontier	Finney	Cimarron	Kiowa
Much drier	0	0	8	11	1	12
Drier	4	0	7	5	4	5
Average	10	1	0	0	7	0
Wetter	3	14	0	0	2	0
Much Wetter	0	1	0	0	0	0
Don't know	0	0	0	1	0	0
	17	16	15	17	14	17
Palmer Index						
Time of Interview	-.33	1.77	-1.57	-3.16	-2.54	-3.60
Previous Month	1.63	1.60	-1.27	-3.61	-2.29	-3.73
Two months prior	1.12	-2.85	-.86	-3.38	-3.50	-3.54

"Would you consider the past few months to have been average, wetter than usual, drier than usual, much wetter than usual, or much drier than usual?" In general the replies of the farmers to this question correspond quite closely to what might be expected when one considers the Palmer Drought Index for the time of the interview and the two months preveding. In Adams, Finney, Kiowa, and Barber Counties the perception of the farmers corresponds very closely with the Palmer Drought Index for the month of the interview. In Frontier County where conditions for the past two months were becoming progressively drier more of the farmers said, much drier than usual, than the mild drought conditions might indicate. In Cimarron County, Oklahoma, half of the farmers spoke of present moisture conditions as average and a couple even said wetter than average. Here there appears to be a tendency to estimate the present conditions by comparison with immediately preceding conditions rather than a longer range average. The result in the case of Cimarron County was for half of the farmers to describe present moisture conditions as average although the drought index indicated conditions of moderate droughts. Another possibility is that they were describing actual rainfall rather than moisture conditions in which case average and wetter than average would be reasonable. The fact that the farmers' perception of current moisture conditions agrees so well with the values of the Palmer Drought Index indicates that this index should be very useful as a base line for comparison with the farmers' perceptions of other aspects of the drought hazard.

Meteorological and Perceived Drought

Although Great Plains wheat farmers are aware of the drought hazard they appear to underestimate its frequency and to overestimate the number of very good years and the average crop yields in such years. Like the hero at the head of the chapter they are eternally optimistic.

The farmers were asked to estimate the number of drought years they would experience if they were to live in their area for 100 years. The averages for each area are seen in Table 10 where they are compared to the actual frequency of drought months of each degree of severity according to the Palmer Index. These values were available on a month-by-month basis for each study

TABLE 10

COMPARISON OF FARMERS' ESTIMATE OF DROUGHT FREQUENCY WITH ACTUAL
DROUGHT CONDITIONS IN THE PAST AS INDICATED BY PALMER INDEX

County	Adams	Barber	Frontier	Finney	Cimarron	Kiowa
Farmers' estimate drt yrs/100	17	16	19.9	28.6	34.8	34.9
% Time drought	42.4	46.9	41.6	47.2	48.7	47.2
% Mild drought and severer	32.8	39.6	32.0	37.0	39.8	34.8
% Moderate drought and severer	23.6	26.8	20.8	26.6	30.8	24.4
% Severe and extreme drought	15.7	13.8	11.2	15.4	18.4	13.4

area from January, 1924 to the time of the interview (see appendix iii). This corresponds to the period in which most of the farmers presently there gained their experience. Only ten of the 96 interviewed started before that date.

One could argue that the Palmer Index measures rainfall variability rather than drought per se. But it takes much more into account than simple variations in amount of precipitation. The close correspondence between the farmers' estimates of present moisture conditions and those of the index, and the fact that even Palmer's incipient drought is noticeable to the farmers in the most humid area suggests that it is valuable as a measure of drought. Further support is provided by the fact that in all areas the more perceptive farmers, according to all other information available, were the ones whose estimates of drought frequency corresponded most closely with the objective measure of the Palmer Drought Index.

There appears to be a clear progression from humid to arid areas in terms of the number of drought years expected in 100, or as it could be interpreted, the percentage of drought years. When the farmers' estimates are compared to the actual percentages of drought months it becomes apparent that all tend to underestimate the frequency of drought. Looking more closely at the two sets of figures reveals an interesting bias. The estimates of drought frequency in the most humid of the study areas (Adams and Barber Counties) correspond closely with the percentage of severe and extreme drought months. In more arid Frontier, Finney, and Cimarron Counties the farmers' figures seem to include the moderate droughts as well. In the most arid of all study areas the perceived percentage corresponds to the figure for all droughts from mild to extreme. This seems to indicate that as aridity increases the correspondence between perceived and meteorological drought becomes closer. It appears that all of the farmers tend to underestimate the frequency of drought and the degree to which it is underestimated increases with increasing humidity.

It is quite clear that meteorological drought is not what the farmers perceive except in the more arid areas. Probably on a very large scale there is, as Palmer assumes, an adjustment of the established economy of any area to the average climate of the area. But since the same crops are grown over a wide area, there are differences in the fineness of the adjustment. Thus in the most humid of the areas studied a near-normal operation may be possible with a considerable negative deviation from normal moisture conditions. However, in the drier areas even a slight deviation has a much greater impact and as a result might be more quickly perceived as drought. This may be the reason for the heightened perception of the farmers on the most arid margins.

The farmers appeared over-optimistic in replying to the question, "how often do you expect a very good crop?" However, the questionnaire as originally set up provided no way of knowing whether the farmers were actually thinking of average rather than very good yields. To more precisely determine this the following additional question was asked in the final four

TABLE 11

EXPECTATION AND ACTUALITY OF VERY GOOD CROPS

County	Barber	Finney	Cimmaron	Kiowa
% Years expected	38	36.9	35	36
No. of bushels/acre	27.8	31.3	22.0	24.6

Actual Yields in Bushels/Harvested Acre[a]				
1963	15.0	19.0	7.0	7.0
1962	20.0	26.0	12.2	17.1
1961	30.0	31.0	20.2	22.0
1960	29.0	39.0	15.8	25.0
1959	20.0	21.0	19.5	18.0
1958	29.0	30.0	23.4	18.1
1957	16.0	31.0	15.3	13.4
1956	12.8	15.3	6.1	5.1
1955	5.6	14.3	7.4	6.0
1954	12.3	9.6	5.7	6.0
1953	10.9	8.5	5.2	6.0
1952	22.2	23.3	12.5	12.0
1951	13.1	11.8	6.0	9.0
1950	11.0	10.0	3.4	9.0
1949	12.0	12.4	13.4	12.0
1948	16.3	16.7	9.9	18.0
1947	17.5	23.7	16.3	22.0
1946	18.6	14.1	9.5	21.0
1945	15.2	19.9	7.9	13.0
1944	17.3	14.3	15.2	13.0
1943	14.0	13.6	10.0	18.0
1942	20.0	19.9	13.7	18.0
1941	15.0	14.9	11.6	8.0
1940	10.9	8.6	11.3	7.0
1939	16.3	5.4	7.3	5.0
1938	9.2	10.0	0	12.0
1937	10.8	3.8	0	--
1936	11.0	5.8	4.1	5.0
1935	8.0	3.0	0	7.0
No. of Years Actual Yields Exceeded or Equaled Expected Yields	3	1	1	1

[a]The crop yield figures for each of the counties were obtained from the state offices of the U. S. Department of Agriculture, Statistical Reporting Service. It was assumed that the farmers' figures reflected yields per harvested acre. Had figures for yields per planted acre been used the farmers estimates would appear even more optimistic.

study areas, "What do you think of as a very good crop?" Table 11 compares the results of these two questions with the actual crop yields in each of the areas for the past twenty-nine years. This shows that the farmers were indeed thinking of a very good crop, in fact one larger than any but the most recent bumper crop in their particular area.[1] Clearly there is a tendency to overestimate both the frequency of occurrence of very good years and the yields in such years.

A Measure of Individual Variation in Perception
of the Drought Risk

An indication of the individual farmer's perception of the drought hazard is provided by answers to the question, "If you were to live here 100 years, how many drought years would you expect to have?" The percentage of drought months over the past 40 years for each area was used as an objective standard of the actual drought risk. By comparing individual farmer's perception of the drought risk with this standard based on the Palmer Index, a measure was derived which takes into account the degree to which each individual's estimate deviates in either direction from the actual drought frequency over the past 40 years. (Most underestimated but a few, especially in the arid areas, made overestimates.) This was used as a measure of their perception of the drought risk. The farmers were classified on a one to nine scale with larger numbers indicating greater deviation, hence less accurate perception.

The half dozen most and least perceptive farmers in each area according to this classification were selected. The same number of farmers was selected using deviations from the average frequency of drought years estimated by the farmers in each area. The individuals included in the most and least perceptive categories according to each standard were compared using field notes, other interview information, and intuitive judgment. The results are listed in Table 12. Under the least and most perceptive columns is indicated the standard which most precisely selected that group for each county. In cases where both standards were equally discriminating this is indicated. In only one case did the classification based on the average expectation of drought in each area appear to be the more discriminating. In Frontier County it appeared to more accurately select the least perceptive group. In three other instances it was about equal to the other classification. In all other cases the classification based on deviations from drought frequencies as indicated by the Palmer Index seemed more appropriate. This

---

[1]Only in Barber County do the average yields for the county exceed more than once the yield that the farmers think of as a very good crop. In Barber County there is a very rapid transition in moisture conditions from east to west. Although the study area was chosen as representative of the county as a whole it may be that the averages have been pulled up somewhat by the greater yields in the more eastern portion of the county.

TABLE 12

COMPARISON OF AREA AVERAGES AND PALMER PERCENTAGES AS
STANDARDS FOR SELECTION OF MOST AND LEAST PERCEPTIVE
INDIVIDUALS

County	Most Perceptive of Drought Risk	Least Perceptive of Risk
Adams	Palmer Index	Both Indexes equal
Barber	Palmer Index	Palmer Index
Frontier	Palmer Index	Area Averages
Finney	Equal	Palmer Index
Cimarron	Palmer Index	Palmer Index
Kiowa	Equal	Palmer Index

tends to offer further support to the conclusion above regarding greater
underestimation by those on the humid margins. It provided evidence that
the individual farmers on the humid margins most likely to have good judgment according to all other indications were indeed those who tended to have
higher estimates of the frequency of drought years. In some individual cases
the measure may be misleading due to fortuitous guesses by some farmers but
by and large it appears to discriminate along the dimension desired. The
sample farmers were divided into two groups approximately equal in numbers,
those more perceptive of the drought risk (47) and those less perceptive
(43). They were so classified on the basis of how closely their estimate of
the drought risk corresponded to that indicated by the Palmer Index. These
two groups are used in subsequent sections of the study to provide a rough
estimate of perception of the drought risk for comparison with other variables.

The Role of Aridity

Several variables reflecting various aspects of drought perception
appear to vary with aridity, as measured by the Thornthwaite Moisture Index.
Table 13 contains a number of these, some of which have been previously mentioned. The number of drought years expected in 100 generally increases with
aridity although not in a regular fashion. The six study areas divide into
two groups. In the three most humid areas drought is expected just under
one-fifth of the time while in the three most arid drought is estimated to
occur close to one-third of the time. The percentage of very good years
expected decreases as aridity increases. The only serious exception is
Barber County, Kansas, whose farmers on the average expected a very good

TABLE 13

ARIDITY AND SELECTED ASPECTS OF DROUGHT PERCEPTION

County	Thornthwaite Moisture Index	Drought Years/100	Chances of Drought Next Year (%)	% Very Good Years Expected
Adams	- 9.24	17.0	24	69
Barber	-16.20	16.0	22	38
Frontier	-19.16	19.9	46	52
Finney	-24.44	28.6	48	46
Cimarron	-27.25	34.8	46	35
Kiowa	-31.39	34.9	74	36

crop only 38 per cent of the time. This is much lower than would be predicted on the basis of aridity. It may be due to the fact that continuous
cropping is the rule in Barber County whereas in all the others some form
of summer fallow is practiced.

Some curious results came from the question, "What are the chances
of drought next year?" In general the farmers felt an increasing likelihood
of drought next year with an increase in aridity. The two dry areas were
similar, the drier ones were also close, but the two driest were different.
Although both Cimarron County, Oklahoma and Kiowa County, Colorado, had been
suffering severe drought for equivalent periods of time, the farmers in the
former area gave much more optimistic answers. It is hypothesized that this
difference was due to a series of small showers in November and early December which had a more marked effect on the morale of the Cimarron County
farmers than on soil moisture conditions.

There appear to be differences in the way in which farmers from different areas define drought. They were asked the question, "What do you think
of as drought?" Table 14 outlines some of the elements considered and shows
the percentage of farmers in the various areas who mentioned each in answer-
ing the question. A large proportion of the farmers define drought both in
terms of crop yields and rainfall and often other elements were mentioned as
well. It may be that all of them perceive drought where it most directly affects them. Usually for Great Plains farmers this would mean crop yields although pasture conditions would be most important in some types of operations,
as can be seen in the larger percentages for Barber, Frontier, and Kiowa
counties who define drought in terms of poor pasture. In the driest areas

TABLE 14

DROUGHT DEFINITIONS: PERCENTAGE MENTIONING EACH ELEMENT

County	Adams	Barber	Frontier	Finney	Cimarron	Kiowa
Crop yields	76	80	80	65	67	47
Rainfall	34	56	60	82	74	82
Poor pasture	6	25	20	0	14	29
Heat	29	25	0	6	14	6
Wind	6	19	0	12	21	6
Others	6	0	7	0	7	12

where even slight moisture deficiencies can readily be seen in smaller crop
yields rainfall is more often used to define drought than in moister regions
where the effect may not be quite so immediately apparent. Heat was mentioned
as a factor mainly by those in the two most humid areas. Other ways of defining drought were in terms of economic effects on the community, subsoil
moisture, and insect infestment.

The measure of perception of the drought hazard derived above was
applied to divide the farmers into two approximately equal groups, the more
and less perceptive. Table 15 shows the percentage of farmers in each group
according to areas. The percentage of farmers in the group more perceptive
of the drought hazard increases with the degree of aridity.[1] Aridity is
clearly an important factor in perception of the drought hazard.

TABLE 15

ARIDITY AND PERCEPTION OF THE DROUGHT RISK
(% of County Farmers in Each Group)

County	More Perceptive	Less Perceptive
Adams	25	75
Barber	27	73
Frontier	50	50
Finney	62	38
Cimarron	69	31
Kiowa	82	18

[1]When the Thornthwaite Moisture Index is correlated with per cent
more perceptive r^2 = .94.

The Role of Drought Experience

Many questions arose in the attempt to develop an accurate index of
drought experience for comparison of individual farmers in the six different
study areas. The number of years each farmer had been farming would not be
a good index of drought experience because it would not take into account
differences in the number of drought years from area to area. The Palmer
Index for past years in each area provided a measure of the number of months
at each degree of drought severity. But would the experience of one month
of mild drought have an equal effect on the humid and arid edges? How can
the difference between a month of extreme drought and a month of mild or
moderate drought be taken into account? Is one month of drought in the growing season equivalent to one month of drought at some other time of the year?

It was assumed that fluctuations in wheat yields roughly reflect the
effect of drought though hail, rust, etc. also may be important. Several different measures were compared with wheat yields such as total number of drought
months in the year, total number of drought months in the growing season,
drought months during the fall, and total negative value of the Palmer Index
for the year. None was clearly better than the others and all seemed to vary
roughly as wheat yields. For the sake of simplicity and ease of calculation
the total number of drought months experienced by each farmer was used as an
index of drought experience. That is the total number of drought months in
the area since the farmer started was used as a measure of his drought experience.

Comparison of drought experience with perception of the drought risk
is shown in Table 16. It is apparent that perception of the drought risk im-
proves with increasing experience. However this does not seem to hold true

TABLE 16

DROUGHT EXPERIENCE AND PERCEPTION OF THE DROUGHT RISK

Drought Experience (No. of Months)	Low 0-72	Medium 88-143	High 174 & Over	High (Under 65)	High (65 & Over)
Number of Farmers . . .	30	35	24	12	12
Average age	35.9	45.0	62.5	54.5	70.3
Average perception[a] . .	4.9	4.3	5.1	3.8	6.4

[a]The lower the number here the more accurate the perception.

for the very oldest farmers (those 65 years of age and older) who as a group
appear to be much less perceptive despite their greater experience.[1] Perhaps
the imminence of their retirement makes drought a less vital issue for them,
or perhaps those who stay   longest are those who steadfastly depreciate the
hazard. To test this latter hypothesis a check was made of the fifteen
farmers who failed to mention dryness as a disadvantage. Although the ratio
of local people to newcomers for all areas is 56 to 40, thirteen of the fifteen who failed to mention dryness as a disadvantage came from the local area
and only two from other more humid areas. This indicates that most of the
newcomers do notice the drought conditions and that some of the local people
tend to ignore the hazard, or take it for granted, or at least do not mention it. This tendency to deny being disturbed by the drought conditions
is touched upon again in chapter vii.

When drought experience is compared with the farmers' estimates of
the chances of drought next year, no clear relationship results. The half
of the farmers in each area with the least experience were compared with the
most experienced half after elimination of those 65 years of age and over.
The results are shown in Table 17. In two cases the most experienced have

TABLE 17

DROUGHT EXPERIENCE AND ESTIMATE OF CHANCES OF DROUGHT NEXT YEAR
(%)

County	Adams	Barber	Frontier	Finney	Cimarron	Kiowa
Most experienced	24	35	50	40	40	57
Least experienced	33	22	37	55	54	60

a more pessimistic estimate than the less experienced, in three cases this
is reversed, and in one case both groups provide similar estimates. The
index of drought perception is derived from the farmers' estimate of the

[1]The oldest farmers are all in the group with the greatest amount of
experience and were separated because their answers appeared so atypical.
In addition there is a 4 year gap between the youngest member of the 65 and
over group and the oldest member of the others in the very experienced group
so factors due to old age may be removed. The division is unfortunate since
this leaves the groups unequal in size. However they are best retained as
such groups because between them are great gaps in amount of experience
i.e., the difference of over 30 months between the highest in the medium
group and the lowest in the high group, and 14 months between highest in
low group and lowest in medium. Nowhere else are there such large gaps
in the distribution.

number of drought years per hundred as compared with the actual drought
frequency. Thus, it provides a measure of the accuracy of the farmers'
assessment of the drought risk. Experience does seem to help in making
such an estimate since the more experienced farmers in general appeared the
more perceptive. However, experience does not seem to aid the farmers in
the face of uncertainty, that is, in the task of estimating what the chances
of drought are in a particular year. This is not entirely surprising since
there is no clear consensus among experts on this point.

Remembrance of Droughts Past

To investigate how past droughts are remembered two questions were
asked: (1) when was the last drought in this county, and (2) have you experienced any others? If the answer to (2) was yes, an effort was made to
elicit some comment as to when it was and what it was like.

Many difficulties prevent precise comparison of an objective standard
of the number of droughts and the memories which farmers retain. The Palmer
Index enables one to state the beginning and end of any particular drought
with reasonable precision (see appendix iii) but farmers do not as clearly
delimit them. Most often they label the drought according to the year in
which it occurred. This can lead to confusion if there are several closely
spaced droughts with one ending and another beginning within one year. It
would be difficult to determine which one the farmer was referring to. To
avoid the possibility of omitting droughts mentioned, ambiguous cases were
classified in as many ways as seemed reasonable. For example, if the farmer
said 1950 and there were two droughts touching that year, both would be included; or if he said "the 50s," all droughts within that decade would be
included. The result was that many minor droughts appeared to be more mentioned than the farmers might have meant. Only a rough classification was
possible under the circumstances. Table 18 indicates only those droughts
which were mentioned by at least half of the farmers present at the time of
its occurrence. It can readily be seen that only the most recent and severe
droughts are included. If the most recent ones are omitted, the remainder
are all extreme droughts. Furthermore, all the extreme droughts are included but no droughts of lesser severity except the severe drought of
September 1931 to July 1933 in Finney County, Kansas. This was included
as part of the drought of the thirties.

As the droughts become more remote in time the exact years are not
mentioned as often. Instead they are described as the drought of "the 30s"
or "the 50s" or "the early 50s." These more general terms often include
several droughts separated by short periods of moister conditions.

TABLE 18

DROUGHTS MENTIONED BY AT LEAST ONE-HALF OF FARMERS PRESENT
AT TIME OF DROUGHT

County	Adams	Barber	Frontier	Finney	Cimarron	Kiowa
	'63-'64 (- .88)[a]	'63-'64 (-3.50)	'64 (-1.89)	'62-'64 (-4.18)	'62-'64 (-3.50)	'63-'64 (-3.78)
	'54-'57 (-4.29)	'52-'57 (-5.59)	'54-'57 (-4.74)	'55-'57 (-4.75)	'51-'57 (-4.64)	'54-'57 (-5.35)
	'33-'41 (-6.53)	'32-'38 (-4.27)	'36-'41 (-4.89)	'52-'55 (-4.18)	'32-'38 (-4.99)	'30-'38 (-5.09)
			'32-'35 (-5.61)	'34-'39 (-5.22)		
				'31-'33 (-3.25)		

[a]Maximum severity of the drought according the the Palmer Index is
shown in brackets.

Table 19 shows the percentage of farmers in each area using such terms. The
base used was the number of sample farmers in the area during the final year
of the drought. In the case of "the 30s" this resulted in percentages of
over 100 since many farmers mentioned this period even though they were not
then farming. This could possibly result from some combination of childhood
memories and local tradition. It is interesting to note that the tendency to
use such terms is most highly developed in the more arid areas. In Kiowa
County, Colorado, almost one-quarter of the farmers were already applying the
term "the 50s" to the series of separate droughts which took place during
that decade.

TABLE 19

PERCENTAGE OF FARMERS USING THE TERMS "THE 50s" AND "THE 30s"

County	Adams	Barber	Frontier	Finney	Cimarron	Kiowa
"the 50s" . .	0	0	0	6	8	23
"the 30s" . .	67	75	140	100	160	250

The majority of farmers in every study area spoke of the most recent drought as is indicated in Table 20. This is not particularly surprising since in all cases the most recent drought was currently being experienced
or had just ended. Even in Adams County, Nebraska, whose recent drought would

TABLE 20

PERCENTAGE OF FARMERS REMEMBERING MOST RECENT DROUGHT

County	Adams	Barber	Frontier	Finney	Cimarron	Kiowa
Drought category of most recent drought	Incipient	Severe	Mild	Extreme	Severe	Severe
Per Cent remembering it	69	81	53	77	100	94

be labelled as incipient, 69 per cent of the farmers mentioned it. For the farmers in this area it was the driest spell since February 1957, and by contrast with the immediately preceding weather it was indeed dry. This is reflected in an analysis of those who included it and those who did not as shown in Table 21. The eleven who mentioned this recent drought in Adams County averaged fifteen years of farming experience and include all the farmers (5) who started farming since the last drought in the county. Those who failed to mention this drought averaged forty years of experience in the area. It may be that their backlog of much more serious drought experience would lead them to dismiss the present moisture conditions as a dry spell while those with less experience regard it as more significant because of their lack of preparation. It is interesting to see that even in the most humid area incipient drought is clearly perceived at least when it is preceded by a long period of much moister conditions. Why then do the farmers here tend to underestimate drought as they do? Is it that they see the effects but as long as they get by they tend to forget about them afterwards?

TABLE 21

NUMBER OF YEARS OF EXPERIENCE OF FARMERS MENTIONING AND NOT
MENTIONING RECENT INCIPIENT DROUGHT IN ADAMS COUNTY

	Number	Average Number of Years in Area	Standard Deviation
Mentioned drought	12	14.9	11.7
Did not mention drought	5	40.6	16.6

One exception to the above tendency to remember only most severe and recent droughts could be described as the factor of primacy. That is, farmers are likely to remember the first drought they experience even if it is not extreme or severe. Several times it was noted that one farmer might include a moderate drought which was not mentioned by any other person in his area. Closer examination usually revealed that the drought had occurred shortly after the individual started farming in that area. Table 22 shows the percentage of farmers in each area who mentioned the first drought after their start in the area. A surprisingly high percentage results considering the fact that this includes all droughts from incipient to extreme. It will be remembered that only the most severe droughts were mentioned by at least half of the farmers.

TABLE 22

PRIMACY IN REMEMBRANCE OF DROUGHTS PAST

County	Adams	Barber	Frontier	Finney	Cimarron	Kiowa
% Remembering first drought	41	40	41	29	28	50

Type of Operation and Perception of the Drought Risk

Perception of the drought risk appears to vary with the type of operation. Table 23 indicates the number and percentage of each type of operator who would be included in the most and least perceptive group.

TABLE 23

PERCEPTION AND TYPE OF OPERATION

Type of Operation	Most Perceptive		Least Perceptive	
	Number	%	Number	%
Straight grain	14	61	9	39
Diversified (Grain emphasis)	16	57	12	43
Diversified (Half and half)	12	55	10	45
Diversified (Livestock emphasis)	4	31	9	69

The types of operations are arranged from those most highly dependent on grain to those most highly dependent on livestock. It can be seen that the percentage of farmers included in the most perceptive group goes down as livestock emphasis increases. Since a livestock enterprise can operate efficiently in a much drier area than an operation entirely dependent on grain, it may be that as the farmers become more diversified and less dependent on cash grain crops, they become less concerned with the vagaries of the weather and somewhat less perceptive of the drought risk.[1]

The preceding discussion in this chapter shows that in general Great Plains wheat farmers are aware of the drought hazard and are able to accurately assess the moisture conditions of the moment. However, they tend to underestimate the frequency of drought years, and to be over-optimistic about the number of very good years and the size of crops in such years. All but the most recent, the most severe and longest droughts tend to be forgotten though individuals may recall the first one they experienced. Within the Great Plains there appear to be variations in perception of the drought risk. Those from the most arid areas, those with the most drought experience, and those whose operations are most vulnerable to variations in the weather have a more accurate perception of the drought risk.

---

[1]Similar conclusions were arrived at independently by John Bennett in his current investigations in S. W. Saskatchewan, as indicated in a letter of October 5, 1965.

CHAPTER V

PERCEPTION OF THE RANGE OF CHOICE

This fellow's inspecting his field of which he has apparently
not practiced stubble mulching on. And then during a dry spell and
hard winds, erosion has started in a big way on him. It ruined his
wheat crop and all he can do is start over.

Introduction

The preceding chapter centered on the Great Plains wheat farmers'
perception of the drought hazard, their past memories, present perception,
and future expectations concerning drought, and the ways in which these
vary with aridity, drought experience, and type of operation. The present
chapter focuses on their perception of the range of choice open to them in
dealing with the drought hazard. It should be emphasized that this is the
practical range of choice, what is seen as possible by the farmers, as opposed to the theoretical range of choice which would include all possibilities.[1] The discussion will consist of two parts, (1) perception of the
range of choice in terms of land use or type of operation, and (2) perception of the range of choice of practices and strategies for reducing drought
losses in using the land primarily for wheat.

Perception of the Range of Choice in Land Use

In general Great Plains wheat farmers do not perceive a wide range
of choice in the way they can use their land. Almost half of those interviewed (45 per cent) felt that their present operation was the only one open
to them. The answers to the question, "Could you use the land in any other
way?" are summarized in Table 24. In the drier areas the proportion who
say they have choices in addition to their present land use decreases.[2]

[1]For further discussion of these concepts, see White, Natural Resources Journal, I (1961), 23-40.

[2]When the percentage perceiving other choices as possible is correlated with the Thornthwaite Moisture Index r^2 = .61.

TABLE 24

PER CENT BY AREA WHO PERCEIVE POSSIBILITY OF OTHER
CHOICES IN LAND USE

Other Choices Possible	Adams n	%	Barber n	%	Frontier n	%	Finney n	%	Cimarron n	%	Kiowa n	%	Total n	%
Yes . .	13	76	9	56	9	60	10	59	4	29	8	47	53	55
No . .	4	24	7	44	6	40	7	41	10	71	9	53	43	45

Thus Kiowa and Cimarron Counties, the two most arid areas, are the only two
in which the majority of farmers felt they had no other choice. Over half
of the farmers in each of the other areas saw other possibilities open to
them, while in Adams County, Nebraska, the most humid study area, three quarters
of the sample felt they could use their land in ways other than the present
use. This was the highest percentage in any of the six areas.

The proportion of farmers who felt they had other land use choices
open to them also appeared to vary with amount of drought experience. Table
25 shows the proportion who saw other possibilities in terms of land use arranged according to amount of drought experience. Again the group of farmers
sixty-five years of age or older seems to deviate from the general trend. But
ignoring them for the moment and concentrating on the first, second and fourth
columns of figures in Table 25, it seems that the greater the amount of drought

TABLE 25

EFFECT OF EXPERIENCE ON PERCEPTION OF OTHER LAND USE POSSIBILITIES

Months of Drought Experience	1 0-72	2 88-143	3 174 and Over	3 Age in Years under 65	3 Age in Years 65 and Over
Number	30	38	28	14	14
Number who see other choices . .	19	17	16	6	10
% who see other choices	63	45	57	43	71

experience the lower the proportion who see other choices in land use as possible. It seems likely that as one grows older the possibility of any major
changes become less or it could be interpreted as an increasing awareness of
the environmental limitations with increasing experience.

Proportions perceiving other land uses as possible differ with the type of operation as shown in Table 26. The more diversified operators do not as often think they have other choices. But a high proportion of both the straight grain farmers and those with a heavy emphasis on livestock felt that they had other choices. Irrigators are close to the average in proportions perceiving other choices as possible.

TABLE 26

TYPE OF OPERATION AND PERCEPTION OF OTHER LAND USE POSSIBILITIES

Type of Operation	Number	Number Perceiving Other Choices	% Perceiving Other Choices
Straight grain	27	17	63
Diversified; grain emphasis	29	14	48
Diversified; half and half	24	11	46
Diversified; livestock emphasis	14	10	71
Total	94	52	55
Irrigators	28	16	57

Having seen that the proportions of farmers who consider other types of land use as possible varies with aridity, experience, and type of operation, it now remains to consider how many and what alternative types of operations are thought of as practical possibilities. Table 27 shows by area the practical range of choice of alternative types of operations. A glance at the bottom line of the table is revealing. It shows that the average number of alternatives decreases with aridity, although in all cases the range of alternative types of operations is very restricted.[1] Finney County, Kansas, farmers provide a wider range than might be expected in such an arid area, but this is due to the possibility of irrigation which presently is more highly developed there than in any of the other areas except Adams County, Nebraska. In the latter area irrigation has already been widely adopted and this is reflected in the large number of farmers who saw other crops such as sugar beets, castor beans, soybeans, corn and even potatoes as alternatives. That irrigation widens the range of alternative crops can be seen in the absence of this choice in any of the areas without irrigation except for one

[1]Correlation of the Thornthwaite Moisture Index and average number of alternatives produces an r^2 of .58.

TABLE 27

PRACTICAL RANGE OF CHOICE OF ALTERNATIVE OPERATIONS BY AREA

Choices Seen	Adams n	Barber n	Frontier n	Finney n	Cimarron n	Kiowa n	Total n
More grass	3	1	6	1	2	5	18
Other crops . . .	10	--	1	2	1	--	14
Irrigation	1	1	1	7	2	--	12
More grain	3	4	--	1	--	1	9
More livestock . .	3	1	--	1	--	2	7
More feed	2	3	--	2	--	--	7
	22	10	8	14	5	8	67
Average number of alternatives . . .	1.3	.62	.53	.82	.36	.47	.72

mention in Frontier County of the possibility of growing safflower. In Table
26 it was noted that irrigators were about average in the proportion who perceived the possibility of other types of operations and yet here it seems as
if the presence of irrigation has widened the range of choice. It may be
that once a person has adopted irrigation he is less likely to think of
shifting back to some other type of operation. Those who see alternatives
may see several different ones mainly in the types of crops which they can
raise. Only one alternative was seen as possible by at least one farmer in
each area, and it was mentioned more frequently than any other. This was to
convert to grassland or pasture, something which has often been advocated by
observers of the Great Plains scene. Irrigation was also considered a practical possibility by at least one farmer in each area except Kiowa County,
where such water is not available except in the rare favored spot. The other
alternatives mentioned further emphasize how restricted the range of choice
in type of operation is within the Great Plains as none of them involve more
than a change in emphasis toward more grain, more livestock or more feed.
The various ways of using their land which Great Plains wheat farmers perceive as possible is thus seen to be relatively narrow with an increasingly
restricted range of choice as aridity increases. Many, like the farmer at
the start of the chapter, see no other choices open to them.

Perception of the Range of Choice of Practices and Strategies for Reducing Drought Losses

Within this general framework it is useful to examine the range of
choice of particular practices and strategies perceived as effective in re-

ducing drought losses by Great Plains wheat farmers. Before questioning
the farmers in detail regarding their perception and adoption of a whole
series of practices, the following question was posed. "If a meeting were
held and you were asked to give suggestions for reducing drought losses,
what would you say?" The answers to this question are summarized in Table 28.

TABLE 28

SUGGESTIONS FOR REDUCING DROUGHT LOSSES

	Adams n	Barber n	Frontier n	Finney n	Cimarron n	Kiowa n	Total n	% of Total
Irrigation . . .	12	7	8	6	12	1	46	26
Stubble mulch .	6	3	3	10	2	4	28	16
Summer fallow .	4	2	6	4	1	4	21	12
Conserve all moisture . . .	4	--	2	7	2	3	18	10
Dams and ponds .	3	6	2	1	--	--	12	7
Terracing . . .	2	5	4	--	--	--	11	6
Reduce cattle numbers . . .	--	1	2	--	--	4	7	4
Reduce expenditures	--	2	--	1	2	2	7	4
Government programs . . .	--	--	1	2	2	1	6	3
Keep down weeds.	1	1	--	--	--	2	4	2
Minimum tillage.	1	--	--	1	1	1	4	2
Plant trees . .	--	2	--	1	--	--	3	2
Plant cover crop	--	1	1	--	--	1	3	2
Adapted crops .	--	1	1	--	--	--	2	1
Others	--	2	--	1	--	3	6	3
Total	33	33	30	34	22	26	178	100
Average number of suggestions	1.9	2.1	2.0	2.0	1.6	1.5	1.9	

The nature of the question is such that it would be expected that
the farmers would mention the practices which they thought were most effective. If the number of times a practice or strategy was mentioned is taken
as an index of its perceived effectiveness, clearly the one which is perceived to be most effective is irrigation. It accounted for over one-quarter
of the total number of suggestions, had the most mentions in all but two of
the areas, and was 10 per cent higher than the one next in line. In Cimarron

County, Oklahoma, it made up over half of the total number of suggestions. The only other practices mentioned by at least one farmer from each area are stubble mulch (16 per cent) and summer fallow (12 per cent). The former was considered the most effective single practice by the farmers in Finney County, Kansas, and along with summer fallow and reduction of cattle numbers was the most mentioned in Kiowa County, Colorado. Both of these practices are highly recommended and widely adopted in all the study areas. The general principle, conserve all moisture, was the remaining suggestion which accounted for as much as 10 per cent of the total. None of the other practices and strategies were mentioned in all areas and none accounted for more than 7 per cent of the total. Dams and ponds were most often suggested in the three most humid counties and often there was the implicit assumption or clear assertion that this would help draw water. The same idea was several times stated as one of the advantages of irrigation. Terracing was also mentioned only in the most humid areas where it has been more widely adopted. Reduction of cattle numbers was a suggestion confined to the counties where cattle are more common. Several means of reducing drought losses, more frequently mentioned in the drier areas, are for the farmer to reduce expenditures, various types of government programs, and minimum tillage to reduce moisture losses. In the category labelled others were such varied suggestions as pray, hire a weather modifier, eliminate poorer operators, keep reserves, insurance, and quit farming.'

But the last line of Table 28 tells a good part of the story. The range of choice of practices or strategies considered effective for reducing drought losses is quite restricted for the individual farmer. The highest number of suggestions given by any farmer was five, and over one-third mentioned only one or none at all. The average number of suggestions for all farmers was just under two, and in the two driest areas it was even less.[1] This parallels the increasingly restricted range of choice in type of operation with increasing aridity.

In all areas the local officials (county agents and SCS officials) recommended the following practices; stubble mulch, summer fallow (though there were some variations in frequency recommended), planting more than one variety, correct seeding date, and all agreed that burning the stubble was a bad practice. These were the only practices among those covered in the study which were recommended by the local officials in the two driest areas. In the remaining four counties terracing was added to this basic

[1]Correlation of the Thornthwaite Moisture Index and average number of suggestions for reducing drought losses produces an r^2 of .48.

list of recommended practices. One additional practice was recommended in
each of the two most humid counties, strip cropping in one, fertilization in
the other. The number of practices recommended in each area by local officials is somewhat larger than the number of suggestions for reducing drought
losses given by the farmers which might be expected since the farmers gave
their suggestions before being asked more specifically about each practice
while the local experts were asked to indicate which practices in the questionnaire they would recommend for their area. But it illustrates that local
experts, as well as farmers, view the range of choice as more restricted in
the more arid areas.

CHAPTER VI

PERCEPTION, ADOPTION AND ADAPTATION

Well he's kinda entering a drought area here. This is about th
first year of a real drought he's had. He's had a crop planted and
is out there to see what is left. Real bad wind erosion here. . . .
If this is a wheat crop he should be working instead of looking. You
have to try to keep this from blowing even if you're almost sure you
can't when you begin. Again this will come back. Nature will take
care of it if he gives a little help. And he will.

The range of choice of practices perceived by Great Plains wheat
farmers to be effective in reducing drought losses provides the background
for a discussion of what they have actually done to adapt to drought conditions. This discussion consists of five main parts; (1) description of the
degree to which a number of practices have been adopted in the six study
areas and some possible explanations why such patterns prevail, (2) an ex-
ploration of the relationship between perception and adoption of practices,
(3) sutland-yonland differences, (4) attitudes of Great Plainsmen toward
risk, water witchers, and luck as a factor in farming success, and (5) discussion of the current adaptation to Great Plains conditions in the study
areas.

Some Patterns of Adoption

There are several different areal patterns in the degree of adoption
of various practices and strategies for coping with the drought hazard. The
reasons for some of them seem self-evident while others provide more of a
puzzle. Some patterns appear to vary with aridity, some depend more on
other local limitations or possibilities, while still others seem to bear
no relationship to either aridity or local conditions. The per cent of
farmers in each of the study areas who have adopted the practices or strategies investigated are listed in Table 29.

The proportion of farmers who maintain reserves of feed and grain

TABLE 29

PER CENT ADOPTION OF VARIOUS PRACTICES AND STRATEGIES BY AREA

	Adams	Barber	Frontier	Finney	Cimmaron	Kiowa
Reserves	38	19	47	47	71	71
Fertilization .	82	88	67	12	58	24
Stubble mulch .	65	31	87	94	43	76
Optimum seeding date	53	31	80	65	7	24
Plant more than one wheat variety . . .	59	50	80	59	43	35
Summer fallow .	94	--	100	100	100	100
Burn stubble . .	6	6	--	--	7	--
Terracing . . .	24	88	94	6	--	6
Strip cropping .	12	6	13	29	--	12
Irrigation . . .	65	--	12	47	36	12
Diversification	59	100	100	35	64	76
Use of credit .	65	75	73	71	57	77
Off-farm income	65	69	47	53	79	65

varies with aridity.[1] The strategy of keeping reserves on hand is least widely adopted in the two most humid study areas with a low of 19 per cent in Barber County, Kansas. The next driest pair of counties showed higher adoption rates at 47 per cent, while the two driest counties the highest percentage of all kept reserves of grain and feed (71 per cent).[2] It may be that the increasing uncertainty due to weather in the more arid areas leads to this need for reserves. The same need for reserves is reflected in the general increase in size of farms in the drier areas.[3]

[1]When the Thornthwaite Moisture Index is correlated with per cent adoption of various practices the following figures result: reserves r^2 = .63, and fertilization -.58.

[2]This agrees with the findings in North Dakota of Philip J. Thair, "Meeting the Impact of Crop-Yield Risks in Great Plains Farming" North Dakota Agricultural Experiment Station Bulletin 392 (Fargo, North Dakota: June, 1954), p. 33. He found a greater use of reserves in a high-risk area than in a low-risk area.

[3]A study in Mills County, Texas, of farmers' adjustments during the drought lasting from 1950-1957 indicated that the proportion of small farms decreased and that of large farms increased as a direct response to the drought. See R. L. Skrabanek, Vera J. Banks and Gladys K. Bowles, "Farmer Adjustments to Drought in a Texas County," Texas Agricultural Experiment Bulletin B-1005 (College Station: Texas A. & M. University, January, 1964).

The use of fertilizer is a practice which is much less frequent in
the drier areas. There are, of course, great variations in the amount and
type of fertilizer recommended for different areas. Here the question is
simply whether fertilizer of any kind is used or not. Among the sample
farmers in Adams County, Nebraska and Barber County, Kansas, on the humid
margins of the study area fertilization was almost universally adopted.
Frontier County, Nebraska, though somewhat drier still showed an adoption
rate of 67 per cent, but thereafter it plummeted to much lower figures for
the driest areas. Though some of those using fertilization in Cimarron
County, Oklahoma, were irrigators there is still a much higher per cent here
than one would expect in such a dry area. The practice of fertilization is
one which loses its effectiveness when conditions are dry though it may pay
off in moister years even in the driest areas.[1]

An interesting pattern is that illustrated by variations in the
adoption of stubble mulch. It is a system of farming in which the stubble
or crop residue is maintained on the surface for soil protection and moisture
conservation.[2] Sub-surface tillage implements make it possible to work the
soil without unduly disturbing the stubble, though in many cases other types
of tools are used.[3] It is a practice which is highly recommended by experts
and local officials in all of the study areas.[4] The farmers also regard it
as one of the most effective means of reducing drought losses as can be seen

---

[1]An indication of the relationship between soil moisture and effectiveness of nitrogen fertilization is provided by the following quotation,
"Profitable use of nitrogen fertilizer may be limited by the amount of moisture available for the crop. Heavy application of nitrogen fertilizer may
depress yields in dry years. On the other hand, starved plants cannot make
maximum use of available soil moisture." Drought Committee of the Nebraska
College of Agriculture, "Adjusting to Drought, Choosing the Right Cropping
Practices" (University of Nebraska Extension Service Circular CC151; Lincoln:
March, 1957), p. 7.

[2]A. W. Zingg and C. J. Whitfield, "A Summary of Research Experience
with Stubble-Mulch Farming in the Western United States," U. S. Department
of Agriculture Technical Bulletin No. 1166 (Washington: U. S. Government
Printing Office, October, 1957).

[3]A discussion of some of these tools and how they can best be used
is found in C. R. Fenster, "Stubble Mulching with Various Types of Machinery,"
Soil Science Society of America Proceedings, XXIV, No. 6 (1960), 518-523.
Reprinted as University of Nebraska College of Agriculture Extension Service
Circular EC 61-134.

[4]It should be noted that there are wide variations in the way in which
the practice is applied by individuals. In this study there was no attempt
at qualitative evaluations of the farmers' stubble mulch methods although
their remarks indicated variations were present. The figures used here
simply indicate whether the practice was used or not. A guide for apprais-
ing stubble mulching is C. R. Fenster, "Stubble Mulch Judging" (University
of Nebraska Extension Service Circular EC 18-84-2).

in Table 28. But it has gained acceptance relatively recently, mainly since the drought of the fifties,[1] so that the adoption process is still not complete. The pattern shown here may thus reveal some general tendencies in the adoption of a useful innovation over a wide range of semi-arid conditions. On the most humid margins, that is, in Adams County, Nebraska, and Barber County, Kansas, the average per cent of adoption for the combined samples was 48 per cent. Moving westward to the drier areas of Frontier County, Nebraska and Finney County, Kansas, one finds that the adoption was almost complete at 91 per cent for the two county average. Progressing still further westward to the two driest of the study areas, Cimarron County, Oklahoma, and Kiowa County, Colorado, one finds that adoption of the practice dropped from the peak of the middle-most counties to 61 per cent which is still somewhat higher than on the humid margin. It may be that in the driest areas the extreme aridity may in certain years limit the effectiveness of the practice. This is suggested by the frequency with which farmers there gave "too dry, no stubble" as the reason for not adopting it.

The same sort of pattern is found in the adoption of the practice of planting more than one wheat variety each year. As with stubble mulch, the percentage of farmers who have adopted increases from the humid margins to the drier portions but drops off again in the very driest areas even though the practice is recommended for all areas. The pattern resembles that of the normal curve with a peak in the center and diminishing frequencies toward each end.

For each county there is an optimum seeding period which helps to avoid the risk of certain insect pests or disease (mosaic), and to produce maximum yields.[2] The percentage of farmers who plant during this period shows a pattern similar to the two immediately above. Again there is an increase from the most humid to the drier areas followed by a decrease in the very driest edges. But in the case of optimum seeding date the number in the most arid areas diminishes to nearly none. Here the seeding date is dictated by the variations in moisture conditions due to chance showers in the fall. The farmers plant when moisture is available and the county agents concur though they recognize an optimum date should conditions be

---

[1]Guest writing in 1951 fails to mention stubble mulch as one of the recommended methods for soil and moisture conservation. See Buddy Ross Guest, Resource Use and Associated Problems in the Upper Cimarron Area Department of Geography Research Paper No. 19, University of Chicago (Chicago: 1951), p. 115.

[2]C. R. Fenster, "Right Planting Dates = $," Nebraska Experiment Station Quarterly, Summer, 1963, Nebraska Agricultural Experiment Station reprint QR 74.

favorable at that time. In Barber County, Kansas, many of the sample farmers
plant a little early in order to utilize their winter wheat for pasture.

Some practices seem to be either almost universally adopted or generally ignored in any one area. Summer fallow is used by every sample farmer
in four areas, by all but one in another, and by none in the sixth where continuous wheat is the rule. Summer fallow is a method of storing an extra
year's supply of rainfall for the use of crops by leaving the land idle and
keeping down the growth of moisture-consuming weeds.[1] In dry areas this results in increased yields.[2] In Barber County, Kansas, although the county
agent recommendation is for fallow every third year and 75 per cent of the
farmers perceive summer fallow as helpful, they generally do not practice it.
The most common reasons given were that it is not economically efficient or
that they did not have enough land. In contrast to the wide adoption of summer fallow, the malpractice of burning the stubble is absent except for three
single cases in three separate areas. In both the case of summer fallow and
burning of stubble the adoption process is essentially complete and there has
been a reasonable adjustment made to local conditions in terms of the practices.

Strip cropping represents a practice which has not really caught on
in any of the study areas. It is a system of farming which utilizes long,
narrow, alternate strips of wheat and fallow which are placed in a position
perpendicular to the prevailing winds. It seems to prevent wind erosion due
to the sheltering effect of the stubble strips on the bare soil between.[3] In
many areas in the Northern Plains it is universally adopted but very few of

---

[1]T. G. Stewart, "Keep Your Farm Productive by Controlled Summer
Fallow"(Colorado State College Extension Services Circular 116-A; Fort
Collins, April, 1937 [reprinted July, 1944]).

[2]K. G. Brangle and B. W. Greb, "Comparison of Continuous Wheat and
Wheat after Fallow in Colorado" (Colorado State University Extension Service
Bulletin 518-S; Fort Collins, December, 1963). For another type of rotation
using fallow, see D. E. Smika, "Fallow-Wheat-Sorghum: An Excellent Rotation
for Dryland in Central Nebraska: (Nebraska Agricultural Experiment Station
Bulletin SB 483; Lincoln: June, 1964). A detailed study using economic
tools to indicate to wheat farmers at various locations the amount of fallow
they should include in their rotations is that by Dale A. Knight, "Economic
Considerations for Selecting the Superior Frequency of Fallow for Wheat in
Three Locations in Western Kansas" (Kansas State College Agricultural Experiment Station Technical Bulletin 85; Manhattan: September, 1956).

[3]A technical description of the amount of wind erosion with various
types of soil and widths of strips is that by W. S. Chepil, "Width of Field
Strips to Control Wind Erosion" (Kansas State College Agricultural Experiment Station Technical Bulletin 92; Manhattan: December, 1957).

the farmers in any of the six sample areas had adopted the practice though
some from each area perceived its value for erosion control. In the two
Kansas counties the county agents recommended it only for sandy soils subject
to wind erosion. In the two Nebraska counties it was not considered important.
In the two driest areas one county agent said it was not recommended because
the government payments were based on a strip of the wrong width; the other
felt it was impractical with large machinery and that it caused ridges in the
fields. The farmers also perceived a wide range of disadvantages. Those on
the driest margins said it caused ridges in the fields; many in Adams County
where it was once more widely used said it involved too much extra work; in
Barber County the main comment was that there was no wind erosion here and a
wide scattering of these and other reasons, such as, cause insect problems,
were found in all areas. It may be that these reasons reflect areal differences in the utility of the practice or just that when a practice is not perceived as particularly useful, a wide variety of reasons can be found for not
adopting it.

The degree of adoption of certain practices varies more according
to local topography than aridity. This is the case for both terracing and
diversification. The former is a practice in which there is a series of
terraces or gently sloping areas separated by earth banks arranged according to the contour of the land.[1] These slow down the run-off which reduces
the rate of soil erosion and allows more moisture to soak into the ground.
Terracing has been almost completely adopted in both Frontier County, Nebraska,
and Barber County, Kansas, where the effects of erosion can soon be seen on
the slopes which are not protected by this practice. In contrast, the study
area in Finney and Adams counties are relatively flat and although terracing
would be very useful in helping to retain run-off, no immediate ill effects
are apparent in its absence. In these areas very few farmers had terraced
their land. It may be that where obviously necessary to prevent deterioration
the practice is pushed by the local officials and becomes widely adopted but
that in the absence of such clear necessity it receives a lower priority from
local officials and few farmers adopt it. In other words, the farmers respond
to prevent deterioration but do not go beyond to look for latent opportunities
to improve conditions.[2] In both Frontier and Barber counties the local SCS

---

[1]For a description of the best methods of farming terraced land which
illustrates the theory behind them, see Paul Jacobson and Walter Weirs, "Farming Terraced Land," U. S. Department of Agriculture Soil Conservation Service
Leaflet No. 335 (Washington: U. S. Government Printing Office, 1958).

[2]Modified decision-making models as developed by sociologists and
economists to explain practice adoption are used by Joan Tully, E. A.
Wilkening, and H. A. Presser, "Factors in Decision-Making in Farming

officials had carried out vigorous campaigns to convince the farmers of the advantages of the practice and the financial support available whereas in both Adams and Finney counties such campaigns though contemplated had not yet begun. The factor of economic efficiency, not examined in this study, could also be of importance here. In the two driest areas the county agents and SCS officials felt that the problem of wind erosion makes the terraces hard to hold.

All of the farmers in the sample grew grain. Where they had livestock as well, the farm was classified as diversified. The majority of farmers in the Finney County sample have straight grain operations; that is, wheat and sorghum. In all of the other areas at least half of the farmers had livestock in addition to grain. And in the two areas which have greater amounts of rough land which can only be utilized by grazing all the sample farmers had diversified operations.[1] This suggests that the degree of diversification is more effected by local topography than degree of aridity.

Adoption of the practice of irrigation involves a radical change both in type of operation and in amount of investment.[2] Although it is generally recommended by the county agents if water is available, in only one of the study areas did a majority of the farmers irrigate. In Adams County, Nebraska, where there is a stable supply of water at relatively shallow depths about two-thirds of the sample farmers used irrigation. In Finney County, Kansas, just under one-half irrigated and in Cimarron County, Oklahoma, where the water is available at greater depths about one-third of the sample used irrigation. The two who irrigated in the Frontier County sample were favorably situated on the flood plain of Medicine Creek from which they obtained their water while the two in the sample from Kiowa County who irrigated did so in

Problems," Human Relations, XVII, No. 4 (1964), 295-320. They state that where there is not a deteriorating situation an understanding of the adoption of certain practices will require not only a knowledge of the farmer's ability to recognize and understand the potential outcomes of adoption but also, goals and values of the farmer, the farmer's perception of the relationship of the adoption of the practice to the attainment of his goals, and the availability of the means of adoption.

[1]This is supported by the findings of Thair, working in North Dakota, who concluded that "diversification with livestock depends less on the need for security than upon the reliability of the available feed base." Thair, p. 33.

[2]For discussions of some of the problems involved and the recommended methods, see Andrew B. Erhart, Walter R. Meger, and Ben L. Grover, "Irrigation in Western Kansas" (Kansas Agricultural Experiment Station Circular 324; Manhattan, 1958); and L. W. Schaffner, Laurel D. Loftsgard, and Norman Dahl, "Integrating Irrigation with Dryland Farming" (North Dakota Agricultural Experiment Station Bulletin No. 433; Fargo, May, 1961).

other states where they also had operations. Bowden suggested that irrigation development spreads in a randomly patterned way from a central nucleus
within a region. This would fit the cases of the six study areas as Adams
County is part of the major irrigation area of South Central Nebraska; Finney
County is within the South West Kansas nucleus and several Cimarron County
farmers spoke of the influence there of irrigators moving up from the irrigated areas of the Texas Panhandle. In contrast in Barber, Frontier, and
Kiowa Counties, further from major centers of pump irrigation activity, four
of the farmers had adopted the practice. In Barber and Kiowa Counties large
proportions of the sample interviewed perceived lack of water as the reason
for not irrigating (see Table 37).

Seventy per cent of all sample farmers have used credit in recent
years.[1] Thair had previously found that high-risk-area farmers do not use
credit for running expenses to the same extent as do farmers in an area of
lower risk.[2] Although the lowest percentage of adoption was in the second
driest area, the remainder of the results do not support this contention
since none of the other counties differ greatly from the 70 per cent average.

The use of off-farm income as a strategy has been adopted by over
60 per cent of the sample farmers. Here a rather curious pattern is seen
with larger proportions having some off-farm source of income on each of the
edges, both the most humid and the most arid, and lesser proportions in the
middle. It may be that these proportions are more dependent on the opportunities present than the need.[3] However, if the number with some other
source of income is a reflection of the relative need for extra income, these
percentages might indicate the relative success of adjustment economically
to the local conditions. It is interesting in this regard to note that the
kind of curve here is just the reverse of that seen for the practice of
stubble mulch seen above.

Perception and Adoption

Having considered the range of choice of practices seen as effective
by Great Plains farmers and the types of adoption patterns found among the

---

[1]The importance of credit as a tool in Great Plains farm management
is emphasized and guidelines are set up for farmers in Aaron G. Nelson,
"Credit As A Tool for the Agricultural Producer" (Great Plains Agricultural
Council Publication No. 15; Lincoln: University of Nebraska College of
Agriculture, February, 1957).

[2]Thair, p. 13.

[3]Hecht in a detailed study of sidewalk farmers in Morton County, Kansas,
mentions the difficulty of finding off-the-farm jobs. See Melvin E. Hecht,
"Location Factors for Sidewalk Farmers in Elkhart, Morton County, Kansas"
(unpublished Ph.D. dissertation, Dept. of Geography, University of Kansas,
1962), p. 158.

study areas, a question arises as to the role of perception in the decision to adopt various practices. To investigate this question the adoption of stubble mulch is used as the best available example of a useful innovation which is recommended for all of the study areas. It seems reasonable to expect that the practice would not be adopted if not perceived as effective and Table 30 shows this to be true except for the case of one disgruntled

TABLE 30

ADOPTION OF STUBBLE MULCH AND PERCEPTION OF ITS EFFECTIVENESS

| | | Perceive Stubble Mulch as Effective | | |
		Yes	No	Totals
Adopt Stubble mulch	Yes	63	1	64
	No	14	18	32
	Totals	77	19	96

Kiowa County farmer who had adopted it but was not convinced that it did any good. However, perception of the practice as effective does not necessarily lead to adoption. A group of fourteen individuals who perceived stubble mulch as effective did not adopt the practice. Examination of their reasons for not adopting the practice should reveal some of the factors other than perception which effect the adoption process. Of these fourteen, eight said the need for special machinery was the main reason for not adopting. These and the one person who said he did not have enough land probably reflect the effect of an economic constraint which prevents adoption even though the practice is perceived as effective. Another type of constraint is seen in the case of the individual who said that his landlord prefers to have him use the moldboard plow. This one and the two who said it was hard to get weeds all were from the most humid margins where the moldboard plow is still used and preferred by some farmers who want clean fields.[1] It may result from inertia or an unwillingness to give up old ways. One individual

---

[1]The difficulty of controlling weeds and volunteer (especially in wet years) is included as one of the disadvantages of stubble mulch in more humid areas in J. A. Hobbs, R. E. Luebs and Frank G. Bieberly, "Stubble Mulch Farming for Erosion Control" (Kansas Agricultural Experiment Station Contribution No. 644; Manhattan: December, 1960). Other disadvantages listed are: reduces yields in humid areas because soil nitrate content is reduced, and poor stands result when trash interferes with planter operation, and increases the number of tillage operations necessary when wet periods occur and stubble is heavy. See also, conclusions of Zingg and Whitfield.

gave no reason for his failure to adopt and the remaining person said stubble
mulch increased the insect problem.

Perception of the effectiveness of a practice and adoption of it are
seen to be closely related. But what is the relationship between perception
of the drought risk and the adoption of practices which aid in minimizing
this risk? Table 31 compares the adoption of stubble mulch with perception
of the drought risk. Of those who had adopted stubble much 60 per cent were

TABLE 31

Perception of the Drought Risk and Adoption of Stubble Mulch

	More Perceptive		Less Perceptive	
	n	%	n	%
Entire sample of farmers	47	52	43	48
Those who adopted stubble mulch . .	37	60	25	40
Those who neither perceived nor adopted stubble mulch	4	28	10	72

among those found to be more perceptive of the drought risk, and 40 per cent
were from less perceptive group. Those who failed to perceive or adopt stubble
mulch were largely farmers who were also less perceptive of the drought risk.
Apparently perception of the drought risk is related to adoption of the practice of stubble mulch. Those more perceptive of the drought risk are more
likely to have adopted the practice than those less perceptive of the risk.[1]
One might have expected even higher proportions if perception were the only
factor involved in the decision-making process, but as indicated briefly above
this is not the case.

The next question to be considered here is how perception of the
drought risk relates to the degree of innovativeness of the Great Plains
farmer, as classified by adopter categories according to the scheme of Rogers
mentioned in chapter ii. It was possible to classify all the sample farmers
in terms of adopter categories with some degree of accuracy on the basis of
ratings by the county agents and other local officials familiar with them,
self-ratings of the farmers, time of adoption of various innovations as indicated by questionnaire material, and intuitive judgment of the interviewer.

[1]Chi square test results comparing the number who adopted stubble
mulch and the number who neither perceived nor adopted was 2.048. The possibility that such result could have arisen by chance is about 40 per cent.

TABLE 32

ADOPTER CATEGORIES AND PERCEPTION OF THE DROUGHT RISK

	Innovators		Early Adopters		Early Majority		Late Majority		Laggards		Total	
	n	%	n	%	n	%	n	%	n	%	n	%
More perceptive	6	50	6	43	24	69	12	48	3	25	47	52
Less perceptive	2	50	8	57	11	31	13	52	9	75	43	48

Table 32 shows the variation in perceptiveness of the drought risk according to adopter categories. The first thing to be noted is that the most innovative farmers are not necessarily those most perceptive of the drought risk. It may be that other qualities are more important for a person to be an innovator or early adopter (this will be investigated further in chapter vii). One other explanation should be made and that is that there are great variations in type of innovativeness. In extreme cases it would be possible for individuals to be clearly among the first to adopt any new types of mechanical equipment but at the same time be laggards in terms of new crop varieties, or vice-versa. Some take a pride in being up to date in terms of livestock practices but lag behind in dry farming practices. The category any individual was placed in would of necessity be a generalization which ignores this type of variation. The only group who appear to have a much larger than average proportion of the individuals more perceptive of the drought risk is that labelled early majority. The innovator and late majority categories have close to the average proportion of those more and less perceptive of the drought risk while early adopters are weighted toward the less perceptive group. The laggards and late majority contain a high proportion of those who are less perceptive of the drought risk. These proportions would be even higher if six farmers who failed to hazard a guess as to the drought risk were placed in the less perceptive group, for among the six were three laggards, two late majority and one early majority.

Combining the results here with those showing the relationship between perception of the drought risk and adoption of stubble mulch certain conclusions can be drawn. First of all, those less perceptive of the drought risk are likely to make up a large proportion of those who fail to adopt not only stubble mulch but a wide range of innovations. In other words, those who are slow in adopting innovations are likely to have a duller perception of the drought risk. However, the most innovative are not necessarily the most perceptive of the drought risk except where the innovations are directly related to the drought problem as in the case of stubble mulch above.

Sutland-Yonland Differences

In certain stages of the adoption process face-to-face communication is considered to be of great importance.[1] Because of the sparsity of the population and thus greater distances one must travel in order to obtain such face-to-face communication, it was hypothesized that the rate of adoption for yonland areas would be lower than in sutland areas. Those further from the county seat would be expected to have lower adoption rates because they are further from the main sources of information, the change agents, who are stationed in the county seat. Each of these hypotheses is tested below.

Stubble mulch adoption rates are the most suitable for testing the hypothesis for it is the only clear case of a recent innovation which has been recommended for all areas and for which the adoption process has not yet completely run its course so that areal differences are present. Table 33 illustrates sutland-yonland differences in the adoption of this practice.

TABLE 33

SUTLAND-YONLAND DIFFERENCES IN PER CENT ADOPTION OF STUBBLE MULCH

	Sutland	Yonland
Dry study areas	65	31
Drier study areas	94	87
Driest study areas	No sutland in these areas	

The differences appear to run in the hypothesized direction but there are too many uncontrolled factors to accept them as conclusive. In the dry areas, as outlined in chapter iii, Barber County was considered yonland and Adams County, sutland, while in the drier areas Frontier County was the yonland area and Finney County the sutland. In both of these cases the yonland areas are quite different from their sutland counterparts in that they have a more rugged topography and consequently greater emphasis on livestock. It may be that the differences in the rate of adoption of stubble mulch result from this rather than the sutland-yonland differences.

[1]Rogers, p. 99.

TABLE 34

MILES FROM COUNTY SEAT AND ADOPTION OF STUBBLE MULCH

	Miles from County Seat			
	0 (Sidewalk Farmers)	Less than 10	10-22	Over 30 (Suitcase Farmers)
Total number	22	38	30	6
Number adopting stubble mulch	14	26	19	5
Per Cent adopting stubble mulch	64	68	63	84

The variation in adoption of stubble mulch with distance from the county seat is shown in Table 34. There appears to be little difference in the rates of adoption of stubble mulch between the sidewalk farmers who live in the county seat, and those who live less than ten miles away, or at greater distances. This is not in accordance with the findings of Hägerstrand in his studies of the diffusion of innovations in Sweden.[1] But it may be that the county seats are not necessarily the main sources of information about new practices. The most mentioned source of information by all sample farmers was farm magazines.[2] If the small number of suitcase farmers in the sample are taken to be representative of all suitcase farmers one might conclude that they are a more innovative group than any of the others as they show an adoption rate well above the average for all Great Plains wheat farmers in the sample (67 per cent). However many of the suitcase farmers in the sample either lived or farmed in Western Kansas and it will be recalled that 94 per cent of the farmers in Finney County had adopted stubble mulch.

Attitudes Toward Luck, Risk, Weather Modification and Water Witchers

Often asserted, but rarely tested is the alleged gambling spirit of Great Plainsmen. To get at this question each of the farmers was asked to

[1]Torsten Hägerstrand, "The Propagation of Innovation Waves," Readings in Cultural Geography, ed. Philip L. Wagner and Marvin W. Mikesell (Chicago: University of Chicago Press, 1962), pp. 355-368. Originally the article was published in Land Studies in Geography, Series B (Human Geography), Vol. IV (1952).

[2]This may hold true for most of the Great Plains since farm magazines are also mentioned as the primary source of information in a sample of 224 North Dakota farm operators. See John D. Photiadis, "Contacts with Agricultural Agents," South Dakota Agricultural Experiment Station Bulletin 493 (Brookings, 1960), p. 5.

choose among a series of strategies the one which best described his way of operating. The strategies were classified on a scale as high, low, or medium in terms of risk-taking willingness. These are as follows:

1. High:

    If a man takes chances when things look good, the future will take care of itself.

    Too much long range planning makes a man too careful.

2. Medium:

    A man should be cautious, but able to take advantage of opportunities when they come up.

    It is good to plan ahead, but you also have to think about the big opportunities and have the courage to seize them.

3. Low:

    If a man plays it safe in the present, the future will take care of itself.

    The man who plans ahead is the man who will succeed.

Table 35 shows the percentage of farmers from each area whose choice reflected, high, medium and low willingness to take risks. These results indicate that the Plainsmen overwhelmingly choose a strategy which implies a careful form of risk-taking, one which is neither reckless nor rigidly tied down by long range planning considerations. In other words, they feel they must be flexible

TABLE 35

RISK-TAKING WILLINGNESS OF GREAT PLAINS FARMERS BY AREA

Willingness To Take Risks	Adams %	Barber %	Frontier %	Finney %	Cimmarron %	Kiowa %	All Areas %
Low	18	38	13	12	14	6	17
Medium . .	76	56	80	76	86	94	78
High . . .	6	6	7	12	--	--	5

enough to adapt to the changing circumstance but at the same time circumspect rather than rash. Although this medium type of risk-taking is the most common attitude in all areas, the highest proportions are found in the two most arid areas where none of the farmers chose either of the high risk strategies. Perhaps the ones who would take such risks have long since been eliminated.[1]

---

[1] In regard to elimination of farmers, it has been high recently in areas of highest failure of wheat. In a number of communities the turn-over from 1954 to 1961 was more than 50 per cent. Such a high turn-over was also common under pioneer conditions of the past. Letter from Leslie Hewes, September 16, 1965. For an analysis of population trends for the entire

To explore the farmers' perception of the role of luck they were ranked on degree of belief according to their replies to the following: "Some say luck plays an important part in success here and some say it doesn't. What do you think?" The per cent who consider luck to be an important factor are shown by area in Table 36 which also shows the areal variation in proportions believing weather modification and water witchers to be effective.[1]

TABLE 36

AREAL VARIATIONS IN PER CENT BELIEVING LUCK TO BE AN
IMPORTANT FACTOR AND WATER WITCHERS TO BE EFFECTIVE

	Adams	Barber	Frontier	Finney	Cimarron	Kiowa	All Areas
Consider luck an important factor	47	75	53	53	65	76	62
Believe water witchers to be effective . . .	6	59	20	29	35	65	31
Believe weather modification to be effective .	18	6	7	12	36	53	22

Almost two-thirds of all the sample farmers believed luck to be an important factor in farming success. In all but the most humid area over half of the farmers felt luck was important and provided many anecdotes to prove their point such as great differences in yield due to difference in the seeding date which came about by chance.

Great Plains area during the 1950-1960 decade, see Gladys K. Bowles, "An Analysis of Population Trends and Effects on Existing Institutions in the Great Plains," Proceedings of a State of Society Conference for Church Leaders November 17-19, 1964, ed. The Planning Committee (Lincoln: Nebraska Center for Continuing Education, 1965), pp. 43-63. A very interesting study which discusses the adjustments which took place in a Texas county during the drought of the fifties showed that many of the young married people moved out. See Skrabanek et al. Other adjustments noted were: a shift in type of livestock from cattle to sheep to goats, acreage adjustments leading to larger farm sizes, adoption of poultry production as a stop-gap measure (dropped when drought ended), off-farm jobs increased for both farmers and their wives, shift from hired to family labor, and a resurgence of optimism when the drought ended.

[1]When each of these factors is correlated with the Thornthwaite Moisture Index the following results are obtained: luck $r^2 = .29$, water witcher belief $r^2 = .35$, and weather modification $r^2 = .49$.

The percentage of farmers believing some water witchers to be effective is only half as great as the number conceding luck to be a factor. Vogt and Hyman speak of water witching as a way of coping with nature in a situation where the outcome is important but uncertain.[1] They demonstrated that the practice persists where the location of an adequate water supply is attended by anxiety and uncertainty. Table 37 compares the percent believing water witchers to be effective and the per cent who gave no water as their reason for irrigating. The results tend to support the findings of Vogt and Hyman as there is a close correspondence between the percentage of farmers who gave no water as the reason for not irrigating, and the percentage who believed that an effective water witcher could be found in the county.[2]

TABLE 37

PERCEPTION OF LACK OF WATER AND BELIEF IN WATER WITCHERS

	Kiowa	Barber	Cimarron	Finney	Frontier	Adams
% Belief in water witchers	65	59	36	29	20	6
% Saying no water .	65	69	27	12	--	--

Weather modification is not generally believed to be effective by Great Plains wheat farmers. About one-fifth of them thought so; the remainder were neutral or did not believe. Very small numbers are found in all but the two most arid areas. In Kiowa County over half of the farmers felt that weather modification was effective. It may be that as the need for moisture becomes greater, there is a greater likelihood that the farmers will be favorably disposed toward such ideas as weather modification. The obvious implication is that any large-scale experiments along this line would probably be most favorably received in the more arid areas.[3]

The Current Adaptation to Great Plains Conditions

A question is now posed which is very difficult to answer in a satisfactory fashion. How do the different zones of aridity compare in terms

---

[1]Evon S. Vogt and Ray Hyman, Water Witching U.S.A. (Chicago: University of Chicago Press, 1959), p. 211.

[2]Correlation of per cent belief in water witchers and per cent saying no water produced an r^2 of .93.

[3]For further discussion in regard to this subject, see Thomas F. Saarinen, "Attitudes Toward Weather Modification," in W. R. Derrick Sewell (ed.), Human Dimensions of Weather Modification, Research Paper No. 105, Department of Geography, University of Chicago, 1966.

of their adjustment to Great Plains conditions? And what criteria can be
used to judge successful adaptation? There has been in the past a certain
amount of vagueness as to what is meant by a good adjustment or adaptation
to Great Plains conditions though this is what everyone seems to say is
necessary.[1]

One common criterion in our society for assessing successful adjustment is that of income. The gross farm income of the year preceding the
interview was obtained from each farmer. The percentages of farmers from
each area who fit into each of the income categories is shown in Table 38.

TABLE 38

GROSS FARM INCOMES OF SAMPLE FARMERS
(Per cent in each category)

	Adams	Barber	Frontier	Finney	Cimarron	Kiowa	All Areas
$ 50- 2,499 . .	--	--	--	12	14	6	5
2,500- 4,999 . .	29	19	20	--	7	12	15
5,000- 9,999 . .	12	6	20	29	22	12	17
10,000-19,999 . .	41	25	27	29	43	23	31
20,000-39,999 . .	18	25	27	12	14	23	20
40,000 and over .	--	19	--	18	--	23	10
Refused to answer	--	6	6	--	--	--	2

If one tries to generalize in terms of aridity zones no simple pattern is
seen. Three counties appear to have a greater preponderance of the higher
incomes but each is from a different zone of aridity. In addition, all
areas show a great deal of variation with income which range from low to
high. Net farm income would be a more sensitive index as the gross data
gives no indication of whether the individual is operating at a profit or
loss. Perhaps the main thing to note here is the large amount of individual
variation which is found in all areas.

One sympton of maladjustment stemming from the original pattern of
settlement would be dissatisfaction with size of farm. An indication of
this is obtainable from the answer to the question, "Do you think you could
stand poor crops better if you had a larger farm? These are shown in Table 39.

---

[1]Malin says "Because the problem has not been adequately defined, there
is much contradiction, misunderstanding, and some controversy," Malin, The
Grassland of North America: Prologemena to Its History with Addenda, p. 414.

TABLE 39

PERCEPTION OF INCREASE IN FARM SIZE AS A STABILIZING FACTOR

	Adams	Barber	Frontier	Finney	Cimarron	Kiowa
Average acreage	321	1,158	1,375	1,432	1,960	4,290
Per cent saying increase in size would help .	53	31	33	65	50	24

It is clear that the average size of farm becomes larger as one moves to the more arid areas, but this is only part of the picture. In three counties over half of the farmers felt that with larger acreages they would have more stability than with their present operation. These were in order of per cent expressing the need for more land; Finney County, Kansas, Adams County, Nebraska, and Cimarron County, Oklahoma, one from each of the broad zones of aridity. It appears that in addition to individual variations as shown above in relation to income, there are also variations from area to area within any one zone of aridity, in terms of adjustment.

Flexibility, mobility, and reserves were stated by Kraenzel to be the key survival traits for Great Plains farming. By examining the degree to which these are incorporated in the practices and strategies of farmers from the various areas it might be possible to gain some idea of the adaptations which have been made to Great Plains conditions. One weakness of the discussion is that it is strictly limited to practices and strategies for which data was collected and this is far from the full range of possibilities.

Greater flexibility is shown by the farmers in the most arid of the study areas by their use of insurance and the reasons given for variations in crop rotations. Table 40 compares the per cent of farmers from each area who always carry insurance with the per cent who only carry it sometimes. Most of those who always carry insurance take all-risk insurance while occasional users generally use only hail insurance. It can readily be seen that those on the most arid margins are most likely to use crop insurance occasionally, that is, they wait until they have good crop prospects before insuring for hail. All farmers were asked if they varied their crop rotation and if so, why. Those on the humid margins who varied their rotation did so because of government programs whereas those on the more arid regions usually gave as the reason, plant sorghum in the spring

---

[1]For an exceptional discussion of flexibility in the practical farming situation and one which considers plant flexibility, product flexibility and contractual flexibility, see Castle, pp. 10-20.

TABLE 40

PER CENT BY AREA WHO CARRY CROP INSURANCE REGULARLY
AND OCCASIONALLY

	Adams	Barber	Frontier	Finney	Cimarron	Kiowa
Always	47	56	67	53	7	12
Sometimes	--	13	20	13	87	64

if the wheat fails. Both of these practices illustrate flexibility in the
face of environmental uncertainty and both are most common in the most arid
areas. One other practice which clearly demonstrates flexibility is "graze-
out wheat production" in which winter wheat is planted a bit early and used
for cattle pasture during certain stages of the fall and winter. But the
sample farmers were not asked about this practice so there is no way of comparing areas. It was noticed most frequently by the author on the humid
margins of the study area, that is, in Barber County. But this was mainly
due to the fact that Barber County was the last area to be completed and by
then winter wheat was sufficiently advanced to permit grazing.

Much greater mobility is necessary to cover the larger acreages in
a timely fashion.[1] Other examples of adaptations requiring mobility are
sidewalk farming and suitcase farming.[2] Of the sidewalk farmers in the sample,
54 per cent were from the two most arid areas, 37 per cent from the next driest
pair and only 9 per cent from the two most humid study areas. There were only

---

[1]The need for mobility in a dry area was recognized by the rich Eastern
dude who was determined he would grow a garden. "He went to town and bought
hisself a wagon, a big strong wagon with four-inch tires. He put fourteen-inch
sideboards on the wagon, and got a load of good soil. . . . Then he got a good
team of horses, big, fast horses, and he hired a chore boy. Then he planted
hisself another garden in that wagon, and he says to the boy, he says, 'Nick,
I want yuh to keep your eye skinned all the time, day and night. And if yuh
see a cloud, no matter where it is, no matter anything, I want yuh to hitch
up this-yere team and drive like hell till yuh get under the cloud. And if
the cloud does percipitate, then rain'll germinate the seed in the good earth
on this-yere wagon, and damn if I won't have me a garden!'" Despite his wis-
dom in recognizing the need for mobility, "that rich dude, he went plumb, flat
broke, buyin' oats for the horses and axle grease for the wagon." Taken from
Botkin (ed.), p. 84.

[2]One of the prerequisites for the increase in numbers of sidewalk
farmers was the increased mobility provided by modern mechanized vehicles and
implements according to Melvin E. Hecht, "Location Factors for Sidewalk
Farmers in Elkhart, Morton County, Kansas" (unpublished Ph.D. dissertation,
Dept. of Geography, University of Kansas, 1962), p. 27.

six suitcase farmers among the sample. Of these, three farmed in Kiowa
County, two in Finney County, and one in Barber County. The trait of mobility as judged by these samples is most highly developed in the most arid
areas.

Reserves as a strategy has been discussed above and it will be remembered that it increased in frequency in the more arid areas. Reserves in
terms of the psychological readiness for drought is well illustrated by the
answer to the question, "How many years in a row could you hold out without
serious problems?" The average number of years given by the farmers from
Adams, Barber, and Frontier Counties was 2.2, for Finney and Cimarron Counties
it rose to 2.8, and in Kiowa County the avérage was three years. Again there
is a clear association with aridity. Other practices illustrating the use of
reserves are summer fallow and stubble mulch. The former was completely
adopted by all farmers except for Barber County and one individual in the
other humid area, Adams County. Stubble mulch reached its peak adoption
in the middle areas with lesser numbers on both the arid and humid margins.

The key survival traits are probably more common in the arid portions of the Plains but this does not necessarily indicate that these areas
have the most harmonious adjustments to their land and climate. On the arid
margins of the Great Plains the issues are clearer. The farmers, much like
the one in the story at the start of the chapter, know that they are defi-
nitely in a dry-farming area and recognize that nature plays a leading role.
The range of choice is narrow and they must adapt to survive in almost all
years. And precisely because the choices are restricted there is less doubt
as to what must be done. Unfortunately this does not eliminate the uncertainty which on the very driest reaches cannot be overcome as effectively.
This may help to account for relatively greater acceptance of the possibility
of using such experimental methods as weather modification. On the humid
edge of the Great Plains the farmer in a good year can get by without using
moisture conserving techniques or he might even find profitable certain humid-
area techniques which would work if all the years were good. Here as in parts
of the Wakamba area studied by Porter, nature is ambiguous and the agricultural
limits are not clearly defined. The result is that dry farming adaptations
are not quite so common nor is the need as urgent. It may be that the individuals adapt as much as they need to in order to survive as farmers, but
little beyond. In other words, they are concerned with satisfying rather
than optimizing. Thus on the humid margins they do not perceive the drought
hazard so accurately because they can still manage to survive without doing
so.

CHAPTER VII

SOME PERSONALITY CHARACTERISTICS OF GREAT PLAINS FARMERS

That man's out looking at his wheat crop, ain't he?--or else hunt-
ing arrowheads. (Laugh) Dirt blowing. He's walking around to see if
anything's left that he could save maybe. That could be here this
year. He's probably pretty worried about everything. If it was me
I'd say he was worried about that crop to keep him going or something.
He's probably accepted it and is deciding what to do next, whether he
should chisel it or it's blowing on his neighbor, whether he's done
his job as a caretaker of the farmland. What he could have done to
prevent it.

Introduction

The findings in this chapter are mainly based on interpretations of
the stories told by Great Plains wheat farmers to TAT cards. There are five
sections: (1) a consideration of the kinds of themes found in the spontaneous comments made by the farmers during the interview, (2) a discussion of
some of the more outstanding characteristics found in stories including those
for cards not analyzed in detail, (3) and (4) group interpretation of all
stories to two of the cards, Card 1 of the regular TAT series, and Card B,
a drought scene, both of which are described above in chapter iii, and
(5) the relationship between personality characteristics and perception of
the drought hazard.

It should be emphasized that this chapter aims to be suggestive
rather than definitive. Only two cards are interpreted in any detail. Both
of these relate to the way in which the farmers handle the issue of achievement. The topic under investigation, wheat farmers and their perception of,
and adaptations to drought, relates to achievement which in the Great Plains
is related to variations in weather.[1] The most pertinent pictures and those

---

[1]McClelland found that the n-achievement level varied from country to
country and that it correlated very highly with an index of economic development. See David C. McClelland, "The Achievement Motive in Economic Growth,"
Paper delivered at North American Conference on the Social Implications of
Industrialization and Technological Change, Chicago, 1960. See also his

most likely to provide fruitful insights are the ones chosen for detailed
analysis since they are designed to elicit achievement themes. There is no
attempt to examine in equal detail any of the other important psychodynamic
issues. One should bear in mind that even within the cards and characteristics considered only the main themes could be abstracted. The following
is a group interpretation and does not cover all the unique qualities and
individual variations found in any group of this size. The characteristics
discussed below are far from a complete picture of the personality of Great
Plains farmers. But it is hoped that this discussion will suggest possible
interrelationships between some of the personality characteristics of Great
Plains farmers and the environmental conditions under which they work.

Main Themes in Spontaneous Comments

A preliminary approach to the ongoing concerns of Great Plains
farmers is obtained from an analysis of spontaneous comments made during
the course of the interviews. Since these were not solicited, but freely
given, it seems likely that they reflect things which are commonly on the
minds of Great Plains farmers. By studying the nature of the comments as
categorized and listed in Table 41, insights can be gained into these pre-
occupations.

The most striking single concern has to do with the uncertainty
of the area as expressed in such comments as:

Anyone who predicts weather out here is either a newcomer or a fool.

One extreme follows another in this country.

Could farm the same way ten years and never have the same crop.

Hindsight is better than foresight as far as weather is concerned.

Other comments dwelt on single climatic elements like the wind.

Wind is the worst thing. Wind doesn't bother me. It's the threat of
what the wind can do to the soil that bothers me.

Most of the other themes listed in Table 41 illustrate what farmers do in
the face of this uncertainty due to the weather.

A substantial percentage (31 per cent) try to make the uncertainty
understandable by seizing upon some postulated regularity, by using their
own powers of observation to try to understand it, by explaining it in terms
of religious beliefs or faith in Nature, or by placing the blame on other
persons or some impersonal agency. The second most frequent single theme
was the need for some sort of regularity. The range of possibilities sug-

books reviewing n-achievement research, David C. McClelland, The Achievement
Motive (New York: Appleton-Century-Crofts, 1953), and The Achieving Society
(Princeton, N.J.: Van Nostrand, 1961).

TABLE 41

THEMES FOUND IN SPONTANEOUS COMMENTS OF GREAT PLAINS
FARMERS DURING INTERVIEWS ON DROUGHT QUESTIONS

Theme	Frequency n	%
Uncertainty of the area	26	20
Search for climatic regularities . . .	13	10
Humor	11	9
Pride in getting by	10	8
Gambling spirit	10	8
Curiosity	9	7
Religious explanations	8	6
Water draws water	8	6
Need for optimism	7	5
Need for defensive farming	7	5
Faith in nature	5	4
Scapegoating	5	4
Personal theories or practices	5	4
Signs of rain	3	2
Need for credit	2	1
Utopian solutions	2	1
	131	100

gested varies from cyclical theories to explanations in terms of geographical
origin of the drought. Such theories, reflected in similar though more
sophisticated models of scientists, have thus far failed to make climatic
uncertainties certain.[1]

A few examples from interview comments are:

Oldtimers say we can expect them [droughts] every four or five years.

We're getting snow in the mountains and that seems to help quite a bit.
When they don't ski we don't harvest much.

---

[1]The attempt to make the uncertainty certain is explained in the
following manner: ". . . the greater the ambiguity existing and the greater
the ignorance, then the more it is necessary for the organism to create a
strong hypothesis in order to maintain its equilibrium, its homoeostasis, and
to relieve it from anxiety concerning the potential threat which develops
from its ignorance. (Ignorance causes anxiety because the potential, unknown
threat may overwhelm the organism. Dispelling ignorance will reduce anxiety--
and even create constructive curiosity--if it is clear that the organism can
master the situation. If mastery is not certain, anxiety will remain even
after ignorance has gone.)" James G. Miller, "Unconscious Processes and
Perception," in Perception:An Approach to Personality, p. 277.

> Floods in Texas this year, rain here next year. We get moisture after them.

> Ordinarily don't have two in a row.

Some 7 per cent of the comments could be classified as observations based on experience which attempt to explain the weather variations or make them more predictable. They reflect curiosity and a more scientific approach to the problem as in the following:

> Wind is broken by different crops. You can feel the difference in temperature as you go by an alfalfa field as compared to stubble or plowed ground.

> Everything south of Colorado is pretty well soaked up now . . . should help in the summer, no hot arid winds.

> July and August is what's hard on us here.

Of comparable frequency were comments which tended to explain it all on the basis of religious beliefs.

> The Bible says there are seven fat years and seven lean years. That's what I go by.

> We're in the last days before Christ returns. Droughts, tornadoes, cyclones will get worse.

> If you studied your scriptures you'd find out sin is to blame for the whole thing. He uses it for His purposes.

A smaller number had a similar faith in Nature.

> Mother Nature can change you very quick.

Another attempt to make uncertainty certain took the way of scapegoating, that is, finding somewhere to place the blame, such as the government, man's own sins, or atomic bomb blasts.

> I still think the atomic bombs've messed up our weather.

> I'll tell you what caused that one [the drought of the 30s]. Wouldn't pay a man enough to buy gasoline.

One final group could be placed here and that consisted of three separate comments claiming that seagulls circling, a ring around the moon, or an east wind indicated rain. These attempt to make the rainfall predictable by associating it with the above mentioned signs.[1]

Three common themes nearly identical in terms of frequency (9, 8, and 8 per cent) represent a contrast to those just considered. Here instead of a need to make the uncertain certain, the comments indicate an awareness or acceptance of the uncertainties and a certain spirit of adventure in pitting one's self against the overpowering elements. No doubt this is a strong motivating factor in drawing people to and keeping them in the region. The humorous remarks generally show an awareness of the difficulties but these are at least momentarily overcome by an anecdote such as:

---

[1]Western folklore related to signs of rain are discussed in Botkin, pp. 85-88.

> When I first came to Kiowa County I was very eager to make a success of it, so I asked an oldtimer for advice as to planting. The oldtimer replied, "I'll tell you how to succeed in farming. Put some seed in your planter and head east at sunrise. When you get about as far as Dodge City plant it."

The uncertainty remains but the person is undefeated. Some remarks typical of the humorous variety are:

> One thing about this country we always get rain when we need it. Whenever we get it you can be darn sure we need it.

> Always been dry here, sometimes drier.

> This is the only country where a farmer can go broke every year and stay in business all his life.

Pride in the ability to produce wheat or survive under extremely stringent environmental conditions is clearly evident in such comments as the following:

> We can do with the least amount of moisture of any place I know of.

> We can get by on five inches if it falls at the right time.

> If we can get a crop up we can raise it on submoisture.

> We tighten up our belts when it's dry.

As might be expected such remarks were most frequent in the driest areas. It has often been remarked that Great Plains farmers are essentially gamblers, in spirit. Such comments as the following show that the possibility of striking it rich does quite often occur to them.

> Here you can buy land and if you're lucky pay for it in a year or two, or lose it.

> Only plungers make a success of it. 'Course a lot go under.

> Some people seem to go out and make a million over night.

But it is not just the desire to get rich quick which is involved. In addition there is a pleasure in playing with the risks and uncertainty. It is often done for the sheer fun of it as is shown in the following remark made by a wheeler-dealer suitcase farmer.

> I've paid for it, but I've had fun at it.

Somewhat related to the gambling spirit or the keeping up of spirits in order to stick it out are the comments here labeled as the need for optimism. No indication is given of what there is to be optimistic about. It almost appears as if there were some sort of a belief that by being optimistic one magically brings about what one wants. In any case, optimism appears to form one facet of the characters of the farmers with such comments as the following appearing in 5 per cent of all those recorded.

> A fellow has to be optimistic. All we need is a little winter moisture.

> The only way you can get a farmer to quit is to tell him there won't be a next year.

> We joke about it but I think we really do believe that next year will be better. I never look ahead expecting worse.

A series of somewhat less frequent themes could be grouped as attempts to provide a solution to the problem of drought. The range of these includes pseudo-scientific beliefs, common sensical suggestions, utopian proposals, and even one clear case of a superstitious survival from the past. The largest single group of comments here was that which implied that the solution was to build dams, increase irrigation, and plant trees because this tended to draw moisture.[1] Such examples as those below were mainly from the more humid margins.

We feel that irrigation wells and many more dams help to draw water.

The more water there is around the more it draws.

More trees and foliage has a tendency to attract rain.

The need for defensive farming was stressed in 5 per cent of the comments. These took the form of:

Anything can happen. Always look for the worst and farm to that end.

Don't stick your neck out, spread investment geographically.

Main thing is save your money in this country.

Work the ground as if it were never going to rain again.

Some unusual personal notions about practices came out in a few comments such as:

Some years stubble plowed under decays, sometimes it doesn't. Is it because of the sign of the moon at planting?

Two types of comments each mentioned twice were the need for or importance of credit and visionary or science-fiction type solutions such as a pipeline from the Great Lakes to the Plains carrying water one way and gas and oil the other.

From this brief discussion of the spontaneous comments of Great Plains wheat farmers during the interview certain ideas emerge. First, it is abundantly clear that there is a great deal of concern about the uncertainty of the environment. This formed the most mentioned single category of comments which shows their preoccupation with this problem. The Plainsmen do not always act rationally in the face of this uncertainty.[2] But then, at the present stage of technology there are few, if any, ways to overcome the

---

[1]Compare with the conclusions of James E. McDonald,"The Evaporation-Precipitation Fallacy," Weather, XVII, No. 5 (1962), 168-177.

[2]A recent writer on the Great Plains asserts that the people of this region have three courses of action open to them in adjusting to their unique environment, (1) effective adaptation, (2) withdrawal into a shell of ultraconservatism, and (3) outmigration. He states that all three have been used but that too much emphasis has been placed on the second two. See Everett E. Peterson, "Where the Coyotes Howl, and the Wind Blows Free," in Proceedings of a State of Society Conference for Church Leaders (Lincoln: University of Nebraska Press, 1963), p. 25.

uncertainty. The quest for certainty found in so many comments is understandable but often irrational especially when untested, unproven and even erroneous theories are accepted as facts. This was the case for all categories here except for comments based on observation of nature. The series of comments described as accepting the uncertainty started from a more realistic standpoint and illustrate some of the reasons why people are attracted to or remain in the area, i.e., the lure of adventure or the pride taken in surviving in spite of the unfavorable elements. Some of these are discussed more fully in the section which follows. The categories of comments considered as solutions to the problem of drought were not, except for the case of defensive farming, likely to solve the problem, and even this would only help make it possible to survive. It has been suggested that Great Plains farmers have two main aims, the first is short-run survival, and the second long-term maximization of gains. The foregoing discussion suggests that the first one looms largest in the minds of the farmers. One difficulty standing in the way of a more rational adjustment is, not the lack of facts but the frequent lack of distinction between facts and erroneous notions so that both may be acted upon with equal degrees of confidence.

Some Outstanding Themes in TAT Stories of Great Plains Farmers

Among the TAT stories told by Great Plains farmers two main types of themes were noticed more often than any others. These, well-illustrated in the story at the head of the chapter, and discussed briefly below, are determination and humor. Also discussed in this section is attitude toward nature.

A commonly recurring theme was that of an extremely resolute determined individual standing up to the environmental buffeting, fighting back, refusing to give in. This could be considered the prototypic Great Plains hero.[1] Stories with this theme stress the importance of will power and spirit in overcoming the great odds against them as is evident in the following stories.

---

[1]This is apparently not a new characteristic. In 1895 Stephen Crane, employed by a newspaper syndicate, was sent west to give a first-hand report on drought and famine conditions in Nebraska. In describing the Nebraska farmers of that day, he says: "They have a determination to wait until nature, with her mystic processes, restores to them the prosperity and bounty of former years. 'If a man stays right by this country, he'll come out all right in the end.'" Stephen Crane, "Waiting for the Spring," Prairie Schooner, XXXVIII, No. 1 (1964), 15-26. The entire issue is devoted to the Great Plains.

The wind is blowing very badly. The roof is blowing off. The barn is patched up. But the man hasn't quit yet. He's still fighting. He's taking the boys right out into it. I think he'll be there when the rains come again.

. . . from the look of his stance and determination he'd stay and fight it out 'til it did rain and come out all right.

The old boy's just wondering if it will ever be what it used to be. He's not only bucking the wind there; he's also in deep thought. He's out there inspecting it. He's out there. He'll find a way.

There is a tremendous pride in the ability to endure the worst of it without complaint. The next couple excerpts carry this to the extreme as the heroes carry on ignoring the blast of wind and dust.

My impression is the wind's blowing, dust's blowing . . . in the middle of a bad situation. But they seem happy, doesn't seem to bother them.

. . . a lot of people think about those days but it isn't a fear to me because even though we came through it we always had enough to eat and had fun. And I was too young to worry about it and I don't worry about it now.

This pride resulting from sticking it out seems to be sufficiently rewarding in some cases to overcome the desire for easier successes in other areas. Notice in the following story that the farmer realizes he could do better elsewhere but remains because he loves the soil and perhaps the challenge of making a go of it.

. . . Things were pretty rough. He liked the earth and if it was at all possible he was going to stick and make a go of it. He had a lot of determination. Even though he could do better elsewhere he likes the soil.

The number and per cent of farmers who included this theme in a clear form are shown according to area in Table 42. Though pervasive throughout the

TABLE 42

NUMBER AND PER CENT OF FARMERS WITH THEME
EXPRESSION DETERMINATION

	Adams	Barber	Frontier	Finney	Cimarron	Kiowa	Total
n	2	3	0	3	1	8	17
%	12	19	0	19	8	47	18

stories with less obvious variations are not included. It seems to be distributed throughout the samples though the greatest concentration of farmers telling such stories is in the very driest area, Kiowa County, Colorado. But it is not simply related to aridity because the other areas show no clear trend with increasing aridity, and Cimarron County, Oklahoma, has a relatively low number though almost as arid as Kiowa. Table 43 may provide a clue. Here the number of pioneers or first generation farmers within the various areas are compared. The counties with the largest numbers of pioneers also have the highest percentage of farmers who told stories with the theme of determination. However, when a direct comparison is made between pioneers and the theme of determination, the relationship though in the hypothesized direction is not significant. Perhaps some more general community factor dependent on the recency of settlement could explain it.

TABLE 43

NUMBER AND PER CENT OF FIRST GENERATION WITHIN AREA

	Adams	Barber	Frontier	Finney	Cimarron	Kiowa	Total
n	--	6	--	9	3	9	27
%	--	38	--	53	21	53	28

The grim humor of Great Plainsmen has previously been noted by observers of the Plains scene. Examination of their stories to TAT cards does indeed show that humor is a common element. It is beyond the scope of this paper and writer to explain why humor functions to relieve the anxiety brought about by facing a fickle and harsh environment, but because of the frequency of such elements, they are singled out as characteristic. It is a well known fact that people find the mishaps and misfortunes of others rather funny, especially if they have had the same miserable experiences. Perhaps this explains the large amount of humor some of the farmers derived from the predicament of the drought victims in the pictures. The following excerpt does not seem funny at face value, but it is incongruous in relation to the picture and there is no doubt that the farmer who told it was amused:

Someone out examining his wheat during the dust bowl days. (Laugh)

The Plainsmen sense the full pathos of the dust blown scene and laughing at it and themselves provides a much needed release as in the following examples:

. . . He's supposed to have $90 wheat out there but he ain't got nothing but a dirt bank and it's still blowing. . . . One thing he'll have new ground to work with next year. There'll be none of that left.

I bet he's looking to see if the crop's coming up. He's looking pretty close. He's not down on his knees scratching yet, but he will be pretty soon.

This humor is often carried to the realm of the absurd as in this example:

He's out after a big wind storm has blown the top soil off and he's looking for arrowheads.

Another frequent form of humor involves laughing at authority figures as is beautifully illustrated in the following excerpt where Nature, God and the government are all attacked.

> That looks like a typical farmer. [Laugh] He looks like he's had a hard time and he knelt down to say his prayers . . . or else he shot himself. [Laugh] Too bad there ain't a puddle of blood. I'd say there were government controls.

When the instances of humor are tabulated by area they appear as in Table 44. With the exception of Barber County, the three driest counties tend to have slightly more farmers exhibiting this characteristic.[1]

TABLE 44

NUMBER AND PER CENT OF FARMERS BY AREA SHOWING
HUMOR IN THEIR STORIES

	Adams	Barber	Frontier	Finney	Cimarron	Kiowa	Total
n	4	6	3	6	5	7	31
%	24	38	20	38	38	41	33

Attitude toward Nature has been postulated as a significant variable affecting how people view and use the land.[2] On the basis of the types of stories told to certain of the cards (Card 2 of the regular TAT set, and Cards A and B of the drought set) it was possible to classify the farmers in terms of their views of man and Nature. Three categories were used, man over Nature, man in harmony with Nature, and man under Nature. Where the story suggested the attitude that man was in control, that he could overcome or change the situation, and no mention was made of the role of Nature, it was classified as man over Nature. The following excerpts illustrate this type of attitude:

> . . . that man is probably inspecting his ground to see what he should do to it. Probably ended up tilling it to stop the dust from blowing.

> I see a real erosion problem that should be, could be easily remedied with strip cropping or stubble mulch.[3]

---

[1] The correlation of per cent of farmers showing humor and Thornthwaite Moisture Index produces an r^2 of .45.

[2] See, for example, the work of the Harvard University Project, "The Comparative study of Values in Five Cultures," as illustrated in Florence R. Kluckhohn and Fred L. Strodtbeck, Variations in Value Orientations (Evanston: Row Peterson, 1961).

[3] A practice such as stubble mulch involves working with Nature but here it is the attitude which is most important. In the above excerpt the farmer gives the impression that man can overcome Nature. He fails to consider the possibility that despite his best efforts he could be unsuccessful.

. . . He's thinking of some way he's going to control it.

Man in harmony with Nature was the label used for those cases in which there was some explicit mention of the need to adjust to Nature or of the importance of the role of Nature. Usually this involved some combination of the need to work but along with this an awareness that the work might be in vain if Nature did not do her part. This attitude is evident in the story at the head of the chapter which also shows a farmer with a strong sense of responsibility and of the linkages to other areas. Some other examples of man in harmony with Nature are:

. . . Lot of this could be prevented, can be prevented. Not all of it. It'll take different farming practices and nature.

. . . They decided to put it back to grass so it wouldn't blow.

You have to try to keep this from blowing even if you're almost sure you can't when you begin. . . . Nature will take care of it if he gives a little help.

Cases in which the solution depended on Nature, where man was the hapless victim of Nature, or where there was resignation or acceptance of the dominance of Nature, or where there was no suggestion that man could do anything about the drought conditions depicted, were classified as man under Nature. This type of attitude is illustrated in the following excerpts:

Haven't got much to look ahead for, very black. They never will have anything unless it gets better or they move away.

. . . This old farmer is pretty disgusted and he's wondering if it would ever rain or things would get better.

. . . Well there's been a big wind. . . . He went out to his wheatfield to see if there's any chance that there'd be wheat left. 'Bout the most hopeless feeling there is in the world.

He's hoping the wind would cease and the rain or moisture would fall. The per cent of farmers from each area with each of these attitudes toward Nature is shown in Table 45.

Two main features of these results stand out. First, is the proportion of farmers with each type of attitude. The stories of two-thirds of these Plainsmen expressed the attitude, man under Nature.[1] It seems

---

[1]This corresponds to one of the body of convictions said to be held by people in southwest Kansas, namely, "adjustments to economic and social conflicts and catastrophes are, in considerable measure, beyond one's control." Others listed include: live and let live, toleration, change is normal, I wouldn't change jobs with anyone and obligations to others are segmentalized in the sense that past human obligations were total. See E. Gordon Erikson, "Social and Cultural Features" (Economic Development in Southwestern Kansas Part X; Lawrence: School of Business, Bureau of Business Research, University of Kansas, 1953), p. 72.

that the Great Plains environment is sufficiently stressful so that only
one-third of the farmers express feelings indicating either man over Nature
or man in harmony with Nature. The second feature is that the proportion
of farmers with each of these attitudes is not appreciably different from
area to area with the exception of Kiowa County, Colorado. In each case
close to 70 per cent are in the man under Nature category, while in Kiowa
County only 42 per cent are in that group. This county was also different
in terms of the proportion with the theme of determination, and in per cent
showing signs of humor in stories. Kiowa County, Colorado is the most extreme of all the sample areas in terms of aridity. The original sod was

TABLE 45

PER CENT OF FARMERS BY AREA WITH VARIOUS ATTITUDES
TOWARD NATURE

	Adams	Barber	Frontier	Finney	Cimarron	Kiowa	All Areas
Man over nature .	12	6	20	19	15	29	17
Man in harmony with nature . .	18	25	7	12	8	29	17
Man under nature.	70	69	73	69	77	42	66

only plowed up about twenty years ago so that some of the original settlers
that came in at that time are still present.[1] And in recent years there
has been a considerable thinning out of farmers and amount of cropland
farmed as is indicated by the large amounts of conservation reserve acreage within the county.[2] This combination of circumstances may have resulted

[1]It may be that the farmer's attitude toward nature is not an important factor. ". . . success or failure does not depend as much on the
willingness to take chances that there will be sufficient precipitation to
raise a crop or grow grass; nor the mere pitting of one's self against an
adverse nature; but rather upon the degree to which the operator or the
operator and his family have assimilated the necessary agricultural and
managerial education." Letter from Bruce G. Whitmore, Extension Agent,
Kiowa County, February 10, 1966. See also, Bruce G. Whitmore, "Developing
Potential Human and Physical Resources in the Plains Area" (unpublished
Master's dissertation, Department of Education, Colorado State University,
1961).

[2]A series of dot maps of the acreage of land under contract in
the Conservation Reserve Program for various years indicates that Kiowa
County, Colorado, is among the areas of greatest density. See 1961 and
1962 Statistical Summary Conservation Reserve Program of the Soil Bank
(Washington: Agricultural Stabilization and Conservation Service, U. S.
Department of Agriculture, August, 1963).

in a more highly selected group in terms of personality characteristics remaining than in the other areas where most of the individuals are there because they happened to be born there. But time does not permit an analysis
of areal differences in personality. It is now time to turn to a consideration of the group analysis to Cards 1 and B. Both of these cards tend to
reveal how individuals deal with the issue of achievement and thus are pertinent to this study and its focus on farmers and how they perceive and
adopt various practices.

Analysis of Stories to Card 1

Card 1 evoked three main types of stories among Great Plains farmers,
all of which had achievement as the main issue. Each of these story .types
is characterized by a unique starting situation which is coded as the Basic
Stem. To each of these starting situations a number of different reactions
may be given (which are coded as Coping Mechanisms), and a variety of resolutions (which are coded as Resolutions and Outcomes).

The first type of story is one in which people or circumstances are
attempting to force the hero to achieve and he doesn't want to. This would
be expressed in Murray's need to press terms as fused press Achievement
Dominance in conflict with need Autonomy (fpAchDom c nAuto). The following
excerpts from stories illustrate this basic stem:

Looks like his folks are trying to make him take violin lessons. He'd
rather not.

Well I would say he's looking at the violin and saying, "Good Lord, do
I have to practice this some more?"

In the second type of story the hero wants to achieve but is faced
with some sort of obstacle either in himself or outside which make success
difficult or impossible. It is expressed in Murray's need-press terms as
need Achievement in conflict with press Obstacle (nAch c pObs). Some examples of this type are:

. . . an ambitious little boy. His music is a little above him right
now.

Well I don't know what he's doing unless his violin broke down or something's wrong. He acts like he's got troubles of some kind.

Well I'd judge he'd just had a music lesson and he didn't know what to
do about it. He's having trouble and he didn't like it. He's plumb
aggravated.

In the third type of story the hero wants to achieve. In need-press
terms this is expressed as need Achievement (nAch). Clear illustrations of
this type are shown below:

I suppose that's a kid wanting to learn to play the violin.

I'd say it's a boy that's interested in the violin and studying it and
imagining what he might do in the future.

The frequency with which each of these story types was chosen is shown in Table 46. By far the largest number of farmers chose Story Type 1 (fpAchDom c nAuto). Over 60 per cent of them defined the achievement situation as one in which there is an outside press which is forcing one to achieve against one's wishes. His problem is not to satisfy the press to achieve but to resolve the conflict between this press and his own desires.

TABLE 46

MAIN THEMES OF GREAT PLAINS FARMERS TO CARD 1

Story Type	Basic Stem	Number	Per Cent
1	fpAchDom c nAuto	54	61
2	nAch c pObs	24	27
3	nAch	10	12
		88	100

The second most frequent basic stem chosen by 27 per cent of the farmers is that of need Achievement in conflict with press Obstacle (nAch c pObs). Here the hero does want to achieve but some sort of obstacle, external or internal, stands in his way.

The third story type to Card 1, chosen by only 12 per cent of the Great Plains farmers is need Achievement (nAch). In these stories the heroes want to achieve and in contrast to the story type immediately above there are no obstacles to impede them.

Considering only the basic stems it is immediately apparent that achievement is perceived as an issue beset with difficulties. In 88 per cent of the stories achievement is coupled with conflict. Only 12 per cent of these stories present achievement as an unconflicted issue.

Given these starting situations several questions arise in regard to each. How does the hero deal with the situation in which he finds himself? Does he draw upon inner resources or external sources of support? How successful are his efforts? What sort of an outcome is seen? The answers to these questions will be given below in the discussions of coping mechanisms, and resolutions and outcomes.

Table 47 classifies the farmers according to story type and shows the number and per cent choosing active, passive or no coping mechanisms. An active coping mechanism is one in which the hero takes action (including mental). The action may be constructive or destructive but in either case it is initiated by the hero. Some examples of active coping mechanisms are the following:

TABLE 47

COPING MECHANISMS TO CARD 1

Coping Mechanism	Story Type 1		Story Type 2		Story Type 3	
	n	%	n	%	n	%
Active	3	6	5	21	2	20
Passive	26	48	10	42	2	20
None	25	46	9	37	6	60

. . . Just looks like he's trying to figure out how to manipulate it or go about it.

. . . he'll pick it up and practice for a few minutes and then he'll slip out the back door and start playing with the other boys.

I'd say he'll just push it off to the side and forget it . . .

Passive coping mechanisms are those in which the hero may think and/or feel positively or negatively, or may manifest internal conflict, or be acted upon by some outside agency, but he does not engage in any overt activity. Notice in the following example of this type that although the hero feels disgusted and would like to give it up he does nothing more than feel that way:

Looks like he don't care about playing the violin, looks to me. Looks a little disgusted. Looks like he'd like to give it up.

No action is taken though negative emotions are felt. In the next example the hero shows internal conflict but remains passive, doing nothing to solve the conflict.

I'd say that was a moment of decision as to whether to start, stop, or go ahead with it.

One last variation of the passive coping mechanism is that in which the environment presents a positive or negative press without any prior appeal by the hero.

Looks like the little kid is kinda put out because he had to practice his violin lesson. He probably was encouraged by some adult . . .

In all these cases the hero takes no active initiative. He is acted upon by other people or events and responds only mentally or emotionally within himself. The remaining category no coping mechanism is self-explanatory. The starting situation may be stated, and the story carried no further or, some results are announced without an indication of how they came about. More commonly, however, one possibility or several alternatives may be given but then no choice is made, no action is taken. Some examples are:

I suppose that's a kid wanting to learn to play the violin. [The end]

. . . I'd say his desire was to be a violinist probably. Well it looks
as if he might turn out to be a musician from all indications.

He can either make a success of the instrument or a failure. [The end]
Returning now to Table 47, the consideration of the coping mechanisms chosen
by Great Plains wheat farmers for Card 1 stories begins with Story Type 1.
More use passive coping mechanisms here than any other type. Almost half
of the farmers portray their heroes as disgusted, unhappy, put out, bored,
confused, unenthusiastic, or wishing they were elsewhere. But only three
stories out of fifty-four showed the hero taking active steps to resolve
the conflict. Those using passive coping mechanisms do little more than
become somewhat emotionally disturbed without directing these emotions
toward the conflict itself. An almost equally large group show no coping
mechanisms. They are immobilized by the conflict and do absolutely nothing.
If the stories with passive coping mechanisms are combined with those in
which the hero did absolutely nothing they include no less than 94 per cent
of all farmers telling this type of story. This indicates that the group
is certainly not notable for their rational problem-solving approach.

Those who chose Story Type 2, need Achievement in conflict with
press Obstacle (nAch c pObs), were somewhat less likely to employ passive
coping mechanisms or none at all. Close to 40 per cent of the stories illustrate each of these types of reactions to the starting situation of conflict. Approximately one-fifth of the farmers choosing this type of story
did utilize active coping mechanisms, that is, the hero did try to learn
to play the violin or to overcome the obstacle. And one would expect this
since in these cases achievement is their own idea or need and not some
thing imposed from without as in the case immediately above. But even
these failed to follow a rational series of steps for implementation of
their goal. Instead they merely emphasized sticking with it as if this
in itself were sufficient.

I'd say he'd turn out to be a master violinist because he's still
with the violin. He hasn't given up on it yet.

But the fact that almost 80 per cent of the group chose either passive or
no coping mechanisms indicates that even when the need Achievement comes from
within and is not an outside press the heroes still do not generally react
in a rational, active fashion to overcome the obstacle and attain their goal.

Farmers choosing Story Type 3 were most likely to have no coping
mechanisms. The heroes in six out of the ten stories of this type, failed
to do anything to attain their clear goal of Achievement. Two other stories
showed a passive reaction and the remaining two had the hero take active
steps. Of these two latter stories only one was a clear case of a desire
or need followed by logical action leading to the desired outcome.

I'd say it's a boy that's interested in the violin and studying it and imagining what he might do in the future. With a lot of practice why perhaps he becomes a famous violinist some day.

What is so amazing is that this is the only farmer of the eighty-eight who told stories to Card 1 who presented this theme which is considered so characteristic of the broader American culture.

Given these illogical, inadequate and often absent coping mechanisms what sort of resolutions and outcomes do the farmers provide? This is shown in Table 48.

TABLE 48

RESOLUTIONS AND OUTCOMES TO CARD 1 STORY TYPES

Resolution	Outcome	Story Type 1		Story Type 2		Story Type 3		Total	
		n	%	n	%	n	%	n	%
Defc/AutoAfft	Bad	19	35	--	--	--	--	19	22
Auto	Good	8	15	--	--	--	--	8	9
Ach	Good	6	11	8	33	1	10	15	17
rej.Ach . .	Bad	--	--	1	4	--	--	1	1
None	None	21	39	15	63	9	90	45	51
Total .		54	100	24	100	10	100	88	100

Those telling Story Type 1 most commonly ended up with no resolution and no outcome to their stories (39 per cent). The state of conflict remained exactly as it was in the beginning (fpAchDom c nAuto). Nothing had been resolved and there was no outcome. The next most frequent resolution, found in 35 per cent of the stories was that of Deference Compliance accompanied by Autonomous Affect. The hero overtly goes along with the press to achieve but his submission is accompanied by an undercurrent of rebellion which makes it a bad outcome since the original needs have not been satisfied nor are they in the process of being satisfied. The inner resistance of this type of resolution and outcome can be seen in the following examples:

He learned to play the violin but that's about as far as he got.

He'll play but he don't want to. He's not with it.

Well he probably never would make a good violinist because he's unhappy with it.

Two other types of resolutions were given to Story Type 1. Both of these are potentially good outcomes. The first is the type of story ending with the hero attaining autonomy and it occurred in 15 per cent of these stories. Here the hero resolves the conflict by refusing to go along with the press

to achieve and thus gains independence or autonomy. This is classified as
a good outcome since the hero's original need is satisfied. Some examples
of this type are:

> When he reaches the age when he can give it up, assert his authority,
> he'll give it up and be done with the violin.
>
> He don't want to learn to play that thing, a kid that doesn't like
> music. . . . He probably put it in the attic.
>
> . . . he don't care much about it and he'll probably give it up.

The other successful resolution given to this story type is that of achievement. But to be a truly good outcome the hero must convert the press to
achieve into his own need (by means of internal psychological changes), give
up his need Autonomy and thus reach a satisfactory conclusion as in the excerpts below:

> Well if he's interested enough it looks like he'll be a violinist. Looks
> like he's interested. I'll say he took up the violin.
>
> He probably was encouraged by some adult that knows the violin and how
> to play it and became a violin player.

However, of the 11 per cent who provided achievement as the resolution only
half were of this type. The other half of the stories although ending in
achievement had a hollow ring. In these cases the hero suddenly moves from
the conflicted situation to great achievement without any intermediate steps
as in the following examples.

> He's dreading it just a little bit. Chances are he'll make an outstand-
> ing musician.
>
> I don't believe he's facing it with enthusiasm. . . . He probably turned
> out to be one of the world's greatest violin players. [Laugh] At that
> point he didn't look like it but you can't tell about those things.

These could be termed magical outcomes since no logical steps precede the
sudden ascent to extremely high achievement. The heroes become not just
ordinary successes but "outstanding" or "one of the world's greatest." In
the second story above the farmer's laugh betrays his own realization of
the unrealistic nature of the ending.

Almost 40 per cent of the stories in this group end in no resolution indicating that achievement is seen by them as an ongoing problem, for
which solutions cannot be readily predicted. Just over a third end in
Deference-Compliance accompanied by Autonomous Affect. This indicates that
they feel they must go along with the press to achieve but remain resentful
of the necessity to do so. The resistance to the outside press to achieve
is further indicated by the 15 per cent who rejected it outright in favor
of independence or autonomy. It is further indicated by the very few cases
in which the press to achieve was accepted by the farmers and internally
transformed into their own need Achievement.

Story Type 2 (nAch c pObs) has two main types of endings. In almost two-thirds of the cases the story ends with no resolution. The conflict is stated and perhaps the hero reacts in some way but the story is carried no further or ends in a state of uncertainty. This is illustrated by the following stories:

> Probably having difficulty playing the notes if he's got to that stage. I think the future is that he's going to need some help.

> I'd say he was mad at the fiddle 'cause it wasn't working right. If he's got any ambition he'll pick it up and try again. If he ain't he'll throw it over his shoulder and run.

The second ending to this type of story is that of achievement and a good outcome. This was found in one-third of these themes, eight stories in all. In general these achievement stories were more realistic than the same resolution in Story Type 1 above. But here the need came from within so that the goal of achievement could be reached with fewer complications. Two of the eight provided magical outcomes similar to those discussed above but the rest took reasonable steps toward fulfilling the stated need. However, there was a tendency to stress will power, determination, and desire as the means of achieving rather than more concrete goal-directed approaches. This is shown in the excerpts below:

> Probably with enough determination some day he will play it.

> I think he'd be a success as concerned as he seems to be about it.

One other resolution was used by one person choosing this story type. In that case the hero rejects achievement and gives up. This fails to satisfy the need of the starting situation and thus is classified as a bad outcome.

As in the preceding group, achievement is seen as an on-going issue since 63 per cent of those telling Story Type 2 provide no resolution. It is interesting to note that the only other significant resolution is that of achievement, a good outcome, which was provided by one-third of the group. Apparently in this group who want to achieve but see some sort of an obstacle in the way, there is a greater expectation of achievement than in any of the other groups, both those who are pressed to achieve and those who see achievement as an unconflicted need. It seems reasonable to expect greater success to accompany efforts to fulfill one's own needs than needs imposed from outside. And for a Great Plains farmer it might be more realistic to see some obstacles standing in the way of achievement.

Story Type 3 (pnAch) provided the largest percentage of stories with no resolution. Nine out of the ten stories had none. The one remaining gave achievement as the resolution. This was the story cited as the sole example of a common American theme. Again the lack of resolutions indicates an on-going problem.

Overview of Stories to Card 1

So far the discussion has centered on abstracting the ways in which Great Plains wheat farmers define, handle and resolve the issue of achievement. The first step was to show the three main types of themes found in their stories to Card 1, that is, the basic stems. Next came a consideration of the way such situations are handled or coped with. Then for each type of story the resolutions and outcomes were tabulated.

However, the main thrust of the present inquiry is toward generalizing about these men as a group to obtain insights into their actions in the face of drought. What are some of the distinctive characteristics of Great Plains wheat farmers and how do they differ from other groups that have been studied by the same method in the past? Accordingly the discussion now turns to the features common to the majority of their stories to Card 1.

The most striking feature found in these stories is conflict. Table 49 shows the basic stems containing this element. Eighty-eight per cent of the farmers see achievement as a conflicted issue. They are either pressed to achieve and don't want to or want to achieve but encounter obstacles. Achievement for them involves an intense emotional struggle due

TABLE 49

BASIC STEMS CONTAINING THE ELEMENT OF CONFLICT

Story Type	Basic Stem	n	% (of Total)
1	fpAchDom c nAuto	54	61
2	nAch c pObs	24	27
		78	88

to conflicting aims or difficulties which discourage direct goal-directed action. This is an extremely high proportion with conflicted feelings about achievement. It is greater than the corresponding proportion among federal executives recently studied by Sims,[1] and these in turn told much more conflicted stories than business executives as studied by Henry.[2] The way in which the Plainsmen handle this conflict is illustrated in Table 50.

---

[1]Sims using the same group interpretation technique found that 72.5 per cent of the stories of federal executives to Card 1 contained the theme of conflict. See Sims, p. 68.

[2]William E. Henry, "Executive Personality and Job Success," Personnel Series No. 120 (New York: American Management Association, 1948); an extended version of this study appears under the title of "The Business Executive: The Psychodynamics of a Social Role," The American Journal of Sociology, LIV, No. 4 (1949), 286-291.

TABLE 50

COPING MECHANISMS TO CARD 1 STORY TYPES WITH ELEMENT OF CONFLICT

Coping Mechanism	Story Type 1		Story Type 2		Total	
	n	%	n	%	n	%
Active	3	6	5	21	8	10
Passive	26	48	10	42	36	46
None	25	46	9	37	34	44
	54	100	24	100	78	100

Essentially the Great Plains farmers do nothing to solve the conflict they themselves have set up in their stories. Almost half (44 per
cent) do absolutely nothing. Another equally large group (46 per cent) show
only passive coping mechanisms, that is, the hero may become frustrated,
aggravated, unhappy, disgusted, confused, worried, or he may hope, dream,
wonder or imagine but he takes no active steps to overcome the conflict,
and as a result the conflict continues unresolved.

In each of these conflict stories there are two opposing forces.
The hero, if acting logically should choose between two alternatives. Thus,
in Story Type 1 the hero could either give in to the press to achieve and
achieve, or not give in to it and not achieve but maintain his autonomy. In
Story Type 2 he could overcome the obstacle and achieve or fail to do so.
But as Table 51 reveals, less than one-third of these stories are resolved
with either achievement or autonomy. By far the largest number leave the
issue unresolved (46 per cent). Another 25 per cent do not squarely face

TABLE 51

RESOLUTIONS TO CARD 1 STORY TYPES WITH ELEMENT OF CONFLICT

Resolution	Story Type 1		Story Type 2		Total	
	n	%	n	%	n	%
Defc/AutoAfft	19	35	--	--	19	25
Auto	8	15	--	--	8	10
Ach	6	11	8	33	14	18
rej Ach	--	--	1	4	1	1
None	21	39	15	63	36	46
	54	100	24	100	78	100

the issue. Instead they resolve it by Deference-Compliance. In these cases the heroes comply by giving in to the press to achieve but inwardly they rebel so the resolution is unsatisfactory. In stories without conflict a higher proportion of resolutions might be expected. But this is not the case. Even in Story Type 3 where the starting situation is without conflict only one in ten of the stories has a resolution, a further indication that achievement is indeed an unresolved issue for wheat farmers on the Great Plains.

Comparison of the outcomes for the conflicted stories and the unconflicted ones is quite revealing. This is shown in Table 52. The outstanding

TABLE 52

OUTCOMES TO CARD 1 STORY TYPES

Outcome	Story Type 1		Story Type 2		Totals (1 & 2)		Story Type 3	
	n	%	n	%	n	%	n	%
Good	17	31	8	33	25	32	1	10
Bad	16	30	1	4	17	22	--	--
None	21	39	15	63	36	46	9	90
	54	100	24	100	78	100	10	100

fact, regardless of story type chosen, is the high proportion of stories ending with no outcome. This suggests that for Great Plains farmers achievement is an on-going problem, one for which no easy solution is seen. Contrasting the stories containing conflict with those without is interesting for it shows that those who see achievement as a conflicted issue have a higher expectation of a good outcome than those who see it as an unconflicted issue. At least they have more realism in their approach to achievement as shown in the expressed awareness of the difficulties without.

The great intellectual confusion and emotional disturbance found among the stories of Great Plains farmers about achievement could be a reflection of the conditions of the risk and uncertainty under which they constantly live. They generally state the initial conditions as conflicted, then either provide no coping mechanism or adopt an essentially passive attitude. Inwardly they may be extremely agitated emotionally and use such strong terms as "frustrated," "disgusted" or "plumb aggravated" to express their feelings. But there is no simple way to solve the conflict except by leaving. They can work, use the best farming practices, prevent extreme wind erosion, but once they have done this, they still must wait for the rains to come. The lack of a clear solution leads to intellectual confusion which is seen in the common use of such phrases as:

He didn't know what to do about it.

. . . something's wrong. He acts like he's got troubles of some kind.

He's thinking and wondering how in the world he got to be there and why. Having made this tentative interpretation, it is time to look at the stories to Card B which places the farmers in an actual situation of achievement much like the ones they often face in the course of their work. How do the farmers' stories handle such a situation? What sorts of solutions do they provide?

Stories to Card B

Card B with its picture of a lone figure out in the dust and wind depicts conditions which are only too familiar to most Great Plains wheat farmers. This is reflected in the uniformity with which they describe the starting situation or basic stem as shown in Table 53. Over 90 per cent of

TABLE 53

Basic Stems to Card B

Story Type	Basic Stem	n	%
1	pEdepr	80	92
2	pEPhyDgr	4	4.5
3	nGoal (unspecified c pE [hostile])	3	3.5
		87	100

the stories begin with what has been coded as press Environmental Deprivation (pEDepr). The farmers recognize that the scene results from a long term lack of moisture and poses a serious problem for the lone figure out in the wind. They generally assess the starting situation very realistically as is illustrated by the following excerpts with their strong flavor of pronounced environmental deprivation:

There's no question about this blowing dust. Drought conditions unquestionably . . .

Well you have right there another example of a fellow trying to make it on this drought-parched area that he got as a farmer.

That's another dust storm scene. Farmer observing loss of crops due to wind erosion, dry weather.

Oh this guy here was walking out across his land. Things are looking pretty tough. Dirt is blowing.

In addition to the basic stem described above there are two much less frequent types of stories which account for 8 per cent of the stories. The first of these is coded as press Environmental Physical Danger (pEPhyDgr). Instead of long term moisture deprivation, these stories emphasize the very short term danger aspects of being caught in a dust storm or lost on the desert. Some examples are:

> This guy's caught in a dirt storm. . . . He's going to have to find a place to duck in.

> . . . looks like he might be walking across a desert and he may be just about exhausted.

The other basic stem found in only three of the eighty-nine stories to Card B would be described in need-press terms as need Unspecified Goal in conflict with press Hostile Environment (nGoal [unspecified] c pE [hostile]). The person's progress toward some unspecified goal is hampered by the environmental resistance he must overcome, i.e., the wind and dust. Some examples are:

> He's trying to find something in the wind and dust. He's on his way somewhere.

> This looks like a man trying to make his way through a hard wind.

Of special interest for a study of drought perception is the way in which the farmers deal with the drought conditions so clearly recognized in Story Type 1. Here they have placed their heroes in the same kind of situation which they themselves must face in times of extreme drought. That being the case, it is most interesting to see what the heroes do about it, and how the situation is resolved. Table 54 summarizes the kinds of coping mechanisms found in the stories.

Almost half of the stories to Card B had what were classified as active approaches to the problem. This suggests that in a more clearly structured achievement situation the farmers are not quite so likely to adopt passive coping mechanisms. However, it must be strongly pointed out that although classified as active, many of those listed above are very restricted in nature. Only one-quarter of the stories have heroes, who when faced with extreme deprivation express the need for action, for some form of work or construction which will either salvage what is left or prevent the wind from doing further damage (fnWkAch). Some examples of this type are:

> . . . he's looking to see if his wheat had all blowed away. Look and see whether he's going to have to list or chisel it.

> Guy out walking over his fields to see what his prospects are, what he's got to do. He's simply got to work that all up, keep it from blowing away, the sooner the better.

> . . . he's wondering what to do about this ground to stop it from blowing. And if that's what it is he'll go home and hook on a machine and try to stop the soil from blowing.

TABLE 54

COPING MECHANISMS TO CARD B

Active			Passive			Active & Passive			None	
	n	%		n	%		n	%	n	%
fnWkAch	19	24	nESuc	20	25	fnWkESuc	7	8.5	7	8.5
nCog	16	20	conflict	4	5					
nEscape	4	5	fnESucStoic- ism	3	4					
Total Active	39	49	Total Passive	27	34		7	8.5	7	8.5

As a first realistic step toward this kind of action another fifth of the stories stressed the need to look over the fields to assess the damage or see how their livestock were faring. These were coded as need Cognizance (nCog). Implicit was the idea of doing something but it should be noted that in this group of stories no action other than looking was actually taken. Some excerpts of this type are:

> Walking out to see how bad it has blown, I guess.

> He's going out to check, see if there's any crop, the way he's bent over looking.

> He could be going out to check on his livestock.

The most striking feature here in all of these active coping mechanisms is the almost total absence in these stories of any hint that the farmers had considered any course of action other than a return to work, in effect a continuation of what they had been doing in the past, a renewal of effort in the face of the latest environmental blow. This sort of attitude is clearly shown in the following excerpt:

> . . . during a dry spell and hard winds, erosion has started in a big way and all he can do is start over.

Nothing new has been added. It is simply an attempt to restore the status quo, not to change it or to do something else to avoid a repetition of the disaster. It is behavior not unlike that of people living below a volcano who return to the same site after each new disaster.[1]

---

[1] This attachment to place has often been remarked on by geographers as in the following quotation, "People have their violent preferences and prejudices starting in a majority of cases with the conviction that where one was born and lives is the best place in the world, no matter how forsaken a hole it may appear to an outsider." Taken from Edward Ullman, "Amenities as a Factor in Regional Growth," Geographical Review, XLIV, No. 1 (1954), 122.

Among the group of stories to Card B with active coping mechanisms there were, however, a few who did suggest other alternatives. Four out of the thirty-nine expressed the thought of escaping after disastrous crop losses but of these, in only one, did the hero, completely broke and in despair, actually leave the area (see story at head of chapter i). An even smaller number (3), within the coping mechanism coded as fused need Work Achievement, had the hero contemplate changing his methods or type of crop.

Passive coping mechanisms were utilized by the heroes in one-third of the stories to Card B. Another 8 per cent did nothing. By far the largest number of those using passive coping mechanisms, in fact, in one-quarter of all stories to Card B, simply stated the need for environmental succorance (nESuc). There was nothing they could do but pray for rain or sit and wait for a change in the moisture conditions. This is shown very clearly in the following examples:

> This looks like an old dried-out farmer looking at his parched land. And he's going to look up and pray for rain.

> He's hoping the wind would cease and the rain or moisture would fall.

> This old farmer is pretty disgusted and he's wondering if it would ever rain or things would get better.

The waiting for rain should not necessarily be construed as a meek and submissive attitude. Often it was the sort of waiting expressed very clearly in three of these stories where the hero exhibited a stubborn stoical make-up, a certain toughness which enabled him to stay and absorb the hard knocks. These stories were coded fused need Environmental Succorance and Stoicism (fnESucStoicism). Only three of eighty stories were explicit in their statement of this stoicism but the same sort of flavor is common through many others. Some examples of this type are:

> I'd say if he survived, stayed with it, he probably raised some good crops later on.

> More'n likely the outcome's just more experience. Maybe you're not old enough to commence counting these downfalls as experience.

> I've lost some crops. It don't make you feel too good. It generally costs you a little more work and expense and comes out in the end.

Another coping mechanism eloquently expressed by four individuals but present to some degree in many other stories was a reaction of confused feelings, conflict and doubt as to the value of sticking it out. These were simply coded as conflict. The hero does not know whether he should stay or go, he does not know what to do. This is illustrated in the excerpts below:

> He's wondering whether it's worth it all or not. Them were the days when he wondered whether to keep on struggling or try something else.

This guy looks like maybe if he planted crops, why they're gone. He dunno whether it's worthwhile to stay or leave.

The remaining type of coping mechanism is that classified as active and passive. In these cases (seven in all) the heroes explicitly expressed the need for some sort of remedial action but at the same time stressed that this would not be enough, that it was also necessary for Nature to do her bit (fnWkESuc). The farmer can, in fact should, do the necessary work but then it depends on the weather, all he can do is work on patiently and hope. This attitude is apparent in the following examples:

Lot of this could be prevented, can be prevented. Not all of it. It'll take different farming practices and Nature.

If this is a wheat crop he should be working instead of looking. You have to try to keep this from blowing even if you're almost sure you can't when you begin. Again this will come back. Nature will take care of it if he gives a little help, and he will.

The outcomes attributed to each of the foregoing broad approaches to the problem are shown in Table 55. The largest single category is that

TABLE 55

OUTCOMES TO STORY TYPE 1 OF CARD B

Coping Mechanism	No Outcome		Bad Outcome		Good Outcome		Total	
	n	%	n	%	n	%	n	%
Active	24	62	8	20	7	18	39	100
Passive	16	59	3	11	8	30	27	100
Active and Passive .	2	29	--	--	5	71	7	100
None	5	71	2	29	--	--	7	100
	47	59	13	16	20	25	80	100

of no outcome. This holds true whether active or passive coping mechanisms are used, and is a reflection of the basic uncertainty of their situation. More stories end in no outcome than the total for both good and bad outcomes. This is not surprising since there is really no end of the hazard which they may face at any moment in their daily work. Good outcomes are more frequently given than bad outcomes even to the extreme drought scene of Card B. This suggests that the Great Plains wheat farmers are more likely to be optimistic than pessimistic. It is interesting to note the differences in the per cent of good outcomes found in conjunction with each type of coping mechanism. Fewer good outcomes seem to result when active coping mechanisms are employed, than passive ones. But the group with the highest percentage of good outcomes is that where both active and passive are com-

bined. It may be that those who work hard but do not necessarily expect to
dominate Nature are less likely to be disappointed by their experience and
hence provide more optimistic outcomes.

Overview to Both Cards 1 and B

In the immediately preceding section the difference between Cards 1
and B in terms of the number of active and passive coping mechanisms was mentioned. If both of these cards deal with the way the issue of achievement
is handled it becomes necessary to explain the reason for the differences in
the percentage of stories displaying each type as indicated in Table 56.

TABLE 56

COMPARISON OF COPING MECHANISMS FOR CARDS 1 AND B

	Card 1 n	Card 1 %	Card B[a] n	Card B[a] %
Active	10	11	51	59
Passive	38	43	29	33
None	40	45	7	8
	88	100	87	100

[a]The active and passive category is included with the active for
Card B.

Before attempting to do so, it should be pointed out that even
with the broadest interpretation of the word active as in the table above
there still remain 41 per cent who use passive or no coping mechanisms for
Card B. It will be recalled, in addition that many of those coping mechanisms included as active for Card B were extremely restricted in terms of
active, i.e., those classified as nCog (18 per cent of all stories). If
these were included in the passive category it would leave 41 per cent as
active. And if those both passive and active were removed, one-third of
the stories would remain as the hard core group, utilizing active coping
mechanisms.

It seems likely that the way in which achievement is handled in
Card 1 is more truly reflective of the psychodynamics of these men than
Card B's stories. The former provides a relatively unstructured achievement situation whereas the latter presents the farmer with familiar circumstances which affect his level of achievement and for which he is better
able to give a consciously structured response. Yet even in the latter
case, where there is a concrete case for which they have had sufficient

time and experience to work out regular coping mechanisms less than half
were clearly active. And these active coping mechanisms often had an un-
thinking repetitive quality about them.

The foregoing discussion suggests that Great Plains farmers are most
likely to handle the issue of achievement conflict in a passive manner or
do nothing. They may become unhappy, disgusted or upset by the press or
need to achieve, but they do not rationally direct themselves toward solv-
ing the conflict which is aroused. Instead their solution involves holding
on, sticking it out, or staying with it, in the hope or expectation that
eventually things will change for the better with time. But the large
number of stories ending with no outcome as seen in Table 57 shows that

TABLE 57

COMPARISON OF OUTCOMES TO CARD 1 AND CARD B

	Card 1 %	Card B %
Good Outcome	26	25
Bad Outcome	23	16
No Outcome	51	59

there is a good deal of uncertainty about the future in spite of their
tendency to rely on it for improvements in moisture conditions. Further
evidence that both stories are about achievement is provided by the comparison of outcomes. For even though Card B presents them with a familiar
situation and conscious control over their stories of achievement the results are virtually identical to those of Card 1.[1] In addition the basic
stems are similar, for press Environmental Deprivation (pEDepr) could be
recoded as press Environmental Deprivation in conflict with need Achievement (pEDepr c nAch). In both cases (Card 1 and Card B) achievement is a
conflicted issue, and in both cases they do not know how to handle the
conflict, and in both cases the conflict is essentially unresolved. The
Plainsmen exhibit a very tenacious and determined stance in the face of
the drought hazard. But they are much more emotionally involved and
prouder of their ability to be stoical and endure the very real distress
due to drought conditions, than of their ability to seek out solutions or
logical alternative courses of action.

---

[1] Correlation (r^2) at per cent providing each type of outcome to
Card 1 and Card B is .93.

Some obvious implications for future government policy stem from this analysis. First of all, any ideas of resettling Great Plains farmers elsewhere is unlikely to meet with much enthusiasm in the area since the farmers so rarely consider such an alternative and since they take such a pride in sticking it out. Nor, for the latter reason should it be expected that there will be any voluntary diminishing of the numbers of farmers currently there.

A second implication is that new methods may not be readily accepted by large numbers of these farmers since they see success as the ability to hold on until the rains return. Many expressed the sentiment that there is nothing you can do when it gets dry and it does not matter much what you do when there is enough moisture.

This second implication seems to be at odds with the opinions of various Great Plains observers who speak of those in the drier areas as "heads-up farmers" and amongst the most innovative they have observed. It also fails to fit the facts of the very rapid adoption of stubble mulch since the drought of the 50s. But one should bear in mind that the technique utilized is one of group interpretation. In studies of diffusion of innovations in rural areas the proportion of innovators has always been small in relation to total numbers. In any field of endeavor heroes are few and far between.[1] One of the limitations of group analysis is the masking of the wide individual differences to provide a group generalization. In stating that most Great Plains wheat farmers are not actively seeking solutions one is not saying they are less active in this regard than other groups of farmers. It may be that they are more so. But the writer knows of no studies of other groups of farmers with which a direct comparison is possible.[2] Knowing that the majority of Great Plains wheat farmers are not actively seeking direct solutions to the drought problem can in itself be useful for a person trying to introduce new practices. Rather than trying to convince all farmers he could more fruitfully channel

---

[1] For a descriptive example from the Great Plains, see the excellent regional novel of Norwegian pioneers in the Dakotas. Here the indomitable hero is often alone in his attempt to rise above the discouragement of those around him. O. E. Rolvaag, Giants in the Earth (New York: Perennial Library Harper and Row, 1965).

[2] There is one other study which utilized a modified form of TAT test to study potatoe farmers in Rhode Island. But the pictures used were different and detailed studies were made of only a few farmers rather than a group analysis. Irving A. Spaulding, "Farm Operator Time-Space Orientations and the Adoption of Recommended Practices," Rhode Island Agricultural Experiment Station Bulletin 330 (Kingston: University of Rhode Island, June, 1955).

his energies toward certain of the more innovative types through whom the
ideas could eventually diffuse to the others.

Results of Spatial Symbols Test

It has been suggested that among Great Plains farmers certain personality characteristics are commonly found and that these are at least in
part derived from their unique environmental situation. Further evidence
that physical environmental differences may be associated with personality
differences is provided by the results of school children's preferences for
spatial symbols. Beck's spatial symbols test[1] consists of a series of
choices among designs differing in five main dimensions; diffuse-dense,
open-delineated, horizontal-vertical, left-right, and up-down. There appear to be consistent age and sex differences in the pattern of spatial
preferences among populations in which the test has been administered. It
was hypothesized that different types of physical environments might also
affect a person's spatial preferences. Age differences among populations
tested indicate that by the age of 13 or 14 the pattern of spatial preferences has usually been established and thereafter major changes are less likely.
Beck's spatial symbols test was administered to three different Great Plains
junior high school classes consisting of 25 students from Eads, Colorado,
17 from Boise City, Oklahoma, and 21 from Medicine Lodge, Kansas. All of
these are flat plains areas though the Kansas area is slightly more rolling
in topography than the other two. The scores of the three plains groups were
not significantly different from each other, so they were merged to form one
group consisting of 63 persons. This composite group's scores were then
compared with the scores of a Chicago group of equivalent age and size (67
persons). Table 58 summarizes the means, standard deviations, shows the
results of significance tests. It is clear that the two groups differ significantly in all dimensions. The probability that such differences would

TABLE 58

COMPARISON OF SPATIAL SYMBOL CHOICES OF CHILDREN FROM
CHICAGO AND THE GREAT PLAINS

| Dimension | Great Plains | | Chicago | | Values of |
	Mean	Std. Dev.	Mean	Std. Dev.	Students T
Diffuse	1.504	0.180	1.388	0.210	3.3478
Open	1.529	0.161	1.396	0.147	4.8686
Horizontal . . .	1.523	0.138	1.433	0.254	2.4634
Left	1.521	0.169	1.446	0.188	2.3757
Down	1.396	0.166	1.495	0.172	3.3127

occur by chance in two different samples of one population is less than one
in one hundred in the case of each dimension. It seems likely that the vastly
different environments are of some importance in accounting for differences
in test scores. But how much is due to broad rural-urban differences cannot
be stated with any degree of assurance until many more populations have been
tested. In any case the results are significant enough to suggest that
further research into the relationship between the physical environment and
various personality dimensions could prove rewarding.

Personality Characteristics, Perception and Adoption

Having examined some personality characteristics of Great Plains
farmers it is important to see how this relates to previous portions of the
study. The remainder of this chapter is concerned with the relationships
between personality characteristics and measures of perception and adoption.

The nature of the above analysis makes it difficult to state with
any certainty the personality characteristics of individuals. However,
differences in the kind of outcome chosen or attitudes toward nature might
be expected to reflect some of the broad personality differences. Table 59
compares the outcomes to Card 1 with perception of the drought risk as defined above. One would expect to find close to 53 per cent in the most perceptive group and 47 per cent in the least perceptive group since these were
the proportions for the entire sample. However, both those who provided bad

TABLE 59

OUTCOME TO CARD 1 AND PERCEPTION OF THE DROUGHT RISK

	Most Perceptive		Least Perceptive		Total	
	n	%	n	%	n	%
Good outcome	16	67	8	33	24	100
Bad outcome	9	47	10	53	19	100
No outcome	22	48	24	54	46	100
	47	53	42	47		

outcomes and those who gave no outcomes have slightly higher proportions in
the least perceptive group than would be expected. In contrast those who
gave good outcomes have a much higher proportion of the more perceptive individuals than any of the other groups. It will be remembered from the
above discussion that the story type to Card 1 which had the greatest proportion of good outcomes was that coded as (nAch c pObs) need Achievement

in conflict with press Obstacle. In other words, the farmers who were perceptive enough to see the achievement situation as beset with obstacles are
also likely to have a heightened perception of the drought risk. All except
one of the good outcomes were found in stories in which the farmers perceived
the achievement as conflicted. One might generalize to say that the less
perceptive farmers are more likely to provide bad or no outcomes to achievement stories. And it would not be unreasonable to suggest that this probably
reflects the kind of outcome they would experience in their farming.

Attitudes toward nature and perception of the drought risk are compared in Table 60. All have close to the average proportions of more and
less perceptive individuals although it might be hypothesized that those
with the attitude of man over nature might more often be less perceptive
of the drought risk.

TABLE 60

ATTITUDE TOWARD NATURE AND PERCEPTION OF THE DROUGHT RISK

	Man over Nature		Man in Harmony with Nature		Man under Nature		Total	
	n	%	n	%	n	%	n	%
More Perceptive .	7	44	9	56	31	53	47	52
Less Perceptive .	9	56	7	44	27	47	43	48

To test the relationship between personality characteristics and
adoption, a whole series of personality variables are arranged according
to adopter categories in Table 61. The adopter categories used were those
outlined by Rogers and mentioned in chapter ii. All farmers in the sample
were categorized in terms of innovativeness, that is, in terms of the relative speed with which they adopted new farming practices. The classification
derived from the questionnaire was sent to the county agents and various
other local officials who confirmed the accuracy or suggested modifications.

Certain characteristics appear to vary with degree of innovativeness. The proportion of individuals giving no outcomes to stories for
Card 1 shows a consistent increase as one proceeds toward the less innovative categories. Among the laggards 79 per cent of the stories to Card 1
were unresolved as opposed to 43 per cent among the early adopters. The
less innovative appear to be more overwhelmed by the issue of achievement.
The more innovative the person, the more likely it is that his stories contain the theme of determination. Three out of the four innovators showed

TABLE 61

ADOPTER CATEGORIES AND VARIOUS INDICES OF PERSONALITY

	Innovators		Early Adopters		Early Majority		Late Majority		Laggards	
	n	%	n	%	n	%	n	%	n	%
1. Outcomes to Story 1:										
No outcome	2	50	6	43	16	46	14	56	11	79
Bad outcome	1	25	6	43	6	17	4	16	2	14
Good outcome	1	25	2	14	13	37	7	28	1	7
2. Determination . . .	3	75	4	29	6	17	2	7	2	13
3. Attitude toward Nature										
Man over nature . .	--	--	3	21	5	14	5	19	3	20
Man in harmony with nature	4	100	3	21	4	11	3	11	2	13
Man under nature . .	--	--	8	58	27	75	19	70	10	67

this characteristic with lesser proportions in the less innovative categories. The attitude toward nature which seems to separate the innovators from the others is that of man in harmony with nature. All four innovators told stories which stressed the importance of man working with nature. The early adopters showed the next greatest proportion of this type of attitude while the others trailed with somewhat smaller percentages. The three least innovative groups had higher proportions of persons who told stories which placed man under nature.

This brief discussion suggests that certain personality characteristics are associated with different degrees of perception of the drought risk and with individuals showing different rates of adoption of farming practices.[1]

---

[1]For a comprehensive list of some of the factors which have been tested for their relationship to innovativeness, see A. Eugene Havens, "A Review of Factors Related to Innovativeness," Ohio Agricultural Experiment Station Mimeo Bulletin 329 (Columbus: The Ohio State University, 1962).

CHAPTER VIII

THE PROBLEM OF DROUGHT PERCEPTION

Well now this one, I see that every once in a while. The wheat I
planted this fall and after a terrible wind storm it's all blown away.
And I'm looking around to see if there's any wheat left and feeling
pretty blue. I would say from the picture he's already worked the
ground once trying to hold it and lost everything. Quite a picture.
Looks like the end of the trail.

Having arrived like our hero at the end of the trail it is time to
reconsider the original aims and to assess what has been accomplished. What
can now be said about the way in which Great Plains wheat farmers perceive
their major problem, the recurring drought hazard? And how does this affect their adaptation to the physical environment?

The problems of drought perception are illuminated by the study
findings. These have limitations but permit a few firm conclusions. The
major findings are suggested showing how they fit into previous research.
Then the more speculative findings are considered in relation to suggestions
of how future research could help fill missing gaps in our knowledge. The
concluding section deals with practical public policy implications of the
study.

Major Findings

Of the hypotheses set up for testing the following appear to have
been substantiated. Perception of the drought hazard varies in some degree
according to (1) degree of aridity, (2) amount of drought experience, and
(3) personality differences. The strongest single relationship found is
that perception of the drought hazard varies with aridity. As aridity increases so does the estimate of the number of drought years in one hundred,
the expectation of drought next year, and the degree of agreement of the
farmers' estimates with the measure of drought frequency provided by the
Palmer drought index. The greater the amount of drought experience the
more accurate the perception of the drought risk. The types of outcomes
provided for TAT stories are likely to reflect broad personality differences.

138

Study results indicate that farmers more perceptive of the drought risk are more likely to give good outcomes to achievement stores, while bad outcomes and no outcomes are somewhat more likely among those less perceptive of the drought risk.

Neither clearly substantiated nor entirely disproved is the hypothesis that there are sutland-yonland differences in the degree to which various practices have been adopted.

Further insight into the way in which Great Plains wheat farmers perceive the problem of drought is provided by other important study findings. These are the relation of drought perception and type of operation, the tendency to underestimate drought frequency, the relationship between age and perception, and the association of certain personality characteristics with the uncertainty of weather conditions in the area.

Perception of the drought risk varies according to type of operation. Farmers who are not quite so dependent on precipitation are generally less perceptive of the drought risk. Thus farmers with a livestock emphasis perceive the risk somewhat less accurately than those whose main emphasis is wheat.

In general the farmers tend to take an optimistic stance in relation to drought frequency. Almost to a man they underestimate the frequency of meteorological drought. This is especially true on the more humid margins and less so in the drier parts. Conversely they tend to overestimate the frequency of very good years and the yields per acre in such years. In all but the very driest counties the farmers expected many more very good years than drought years.

Age and experience are very closely related. Generally, within any one area, the older the farmer, the greater the amount of drought experience and the more experienced the group the higher the proportion of individuals more perceptive of the drought risk. But this does not seem to hold true in the case of the very oldest farmers, who, as a group, appear less perceptive despite their greater experience.

Frequently found among Great Plains wheat farmers are certain personality characteristics which appear to be associated with the uncertainty of weather conditions in the area. Group analysis of TAT stories told to cards which raised the issue of achievement showed that for Great Plains wheat farmers this is an extremely conflicted issue. The heroes in stories to the general achievement card are most commonly portrayed as in a situation in which they are being pressed to achieve but do not want to, or wanting to achieve but faced with some obstacle which makes achievement difficult. The farmers do not know how to handle the conflict and in most cases

it remains unresolved. The clear parallel between the uncertainty due to the
weather and the uncertain conflictful way the achievement issue is handled by
the Great Plains wheat farmers suggests that at least this area of their per-
sonalities is strongly influenced by the environmental situation which they
constantly face.

Some Findings which Support Previous Research

A few of the firmer findings lend support to previous work in perception of natural hazards. Studies among flood plain dwellers and coastal
residents indicate that experience and frequency of occurrence are important
factors in perception of natural hazards. The persons with more direct experience and those in areas more frequently affected appear to be more perceptive than those with less experience or those in areas where the hazards
occur less frequently. These factors were found to be important in drought
perception as well. The farmers with the greatest amount of drought experience and those in the more arid areas tended to be more accurate in their
assessment of drought frequency, with the exception of the very oldest group.

Burton and Kates in discussing perception of natural hazards hypothesized that heightened hazard perception would be expected where the hazard
is directly related to the resource use. The findings of the present study
offer support for this view. Wheat production, the main resource use in
the Great Plains, is directly affected by the drought hazard. And Great
Plains wheat farmers are certainly aware of the drought hazard. In fact
preoccupation with precipitation seems characteristic. In dry periods
they speak of little else. They live in hope of more rain. Their perception of the present moisture conditions is accurate and they rapidly respond
to even slight changes in moisture conditions. Their perception of the
range of choice in land use and types of applicable practices parallels
the assessment of local experts and shows that they have a relatively accurate appreciation of the differing potentialities or limitations of different areas.

Yet Great Plains wheat farmers consistently underestimate the frequency of drought years just as coastal dwellers were seen to underestimate
the frequency of storm damage. In addition the wheat farmers tend to overestimate the number of very good years and the size of crop yields in such
years. The fact that they tend to forget all but the most extreme droughts
may help to account for such unwarranted optimism.

Some Interesting Unsolved Issues

Seeking to solve the problem of how Great Plains wheat farmers per-

ceive the drought hazard led to consideration of a series of previously un-
studied issues. Some of the questions raised are quite specific and could
be tested directly. Others are more broadly speculative and less easily answered.

How do short-run changes in weather conditions affect the attitudes
and actions of people in drought areas? Many separate measures suggested
that the farmers respond rapidly to even slight changes in moisture conditions. In the sample of Cimarron County, Oklahoma, cited above, it was
hypothesized that a series of small showers had a more marked affect on
the morale of the farmers than on the soil moisture conditions. Could a
rough prediction of the amount of optimism present be made by calculating
the number of days since an appreciable rain?

How does the type of operation affect perception of the drought
hazard? Study evidence showed that the operations more dependent on grain
tended to have a higher percentage of farmers more perceptive of the drought
risk. Could this be extended to predict that livestock operators would be
less concerned and less perceptive of the risks due to drought? This remains to be tested since all farmers in the present study were at least
partially dependent on wheat production for their livelihood, and there
were no comparable studies of farmers in the same area or other areas.

Are there certain personality traits which characterize Great Plains
wheat farmers? If so, what are they? Some traits, often mentioned by
other observers of the Great Plains scene were frequently found among the
present study's sample of farmers. These include the theme of determination or sticking it out, the humor related to the dust and drought, and an
attitude of man under nature suggesting a feeling of helplessness in the
face of the environmental hazard. But whether these traits are more common
here than elsewhere can not be stated with a high degree of certainty until
similar studies are made of other groups, both farmers and non-farmers.

The close parallel between environmental uncertainty and the way
in which Great Plains wheat farmers handle the issue of achievement leads
to the larger question of the effects of the impersonal environment on the
psychodynamics of the individual or groups of individuals. Would other
groups with different environmental circumstances handle the issue of achievement differently? Are there other facets of personality which might be
similarly affected? This study's results suggest that the TAT may prove
to be a useful tool for further investigations along this line.

Another question concerning the Great Plains which has broader implications is that of the relative degree of adjustment of various areas.
It was suggested that where clearly necessary for survival a larger number

of adjustments are made. However where the environmental possibilities are less clearly delineated and where it is possible to survive without making as many adjustments they are not made and the hazard is not as clearly perceived. Although the role of economic efficiency was not directly examined in this study considerable evidence indicated that in general the Great Plains wheat farmers appear to be more concerned with satisficing than with maximization of profits or developing the resource base to the optimal level. More detailed investigations might reveal the degree to which the farmers are open to niceties in adjustment to environmental variations. The wide variety of different patterns of adaptation of specific dry farming practices suggests that there are many variables interacting which are not clearly understood.

Some Implications for Public Policy

Certain of the study findings suggest guidelines for persons interested in enhancing the resource manager's awareness of the drought hazard. Since the farmers are generally aware of the drought hazard there would be no value in re-emphasizing that the area is drought prone. However it might prove helpful to point out to all farmers the frequency with which drought occurs and the effects which result including those which are less than catastrophic. The more humid areas and the less experienced farmers should benefit the most from such information.

Because of the tendency to forget dry periods after they have passed more success might attend campaigns to introduce new practices if they take place in periods of dry weather.

A certain resistance to the adoption of new practices may result from a feeling of helplessness in the face of nature, a "what's the use" attitude, and the fact that many see success as the ability to hold on until the rains return, rather than finding new methods to deal with drought. Because of this type of resistance public officials might achieve more success if they concentrated their efforts among some of the more innovative farmers from whom the practices could later diffuse to other members of the community.

Perception appears to be one of the important factors in the decision of Great Plains wheat farmers to adopt such practices as stubble mulch. It follows that public officials concerned with the spread of innovations or other modifications of resource use could gain insights as to procedure by investigating exactly how the resource manager perceives the hazard and the choice open to him.

APPENDIX I

A GLOSSARY OF DROUGHT DEFINITIONS

General

drought (common usage) reflects the relative insecurity of mankind in the
face of a natural phenomenon that he does not understand thoroughly and
for which, therefore, he has not devised adequate protective measures.

> Thomas, H.E. "General Summary of Effects of Drought in the Southwest,"
> Geological Survey Professional Paper 372-H (Washington: U. S. Govern-
> ment Printing Office, 1963), p. 2.

Drought (drout) [ME drougth, drugthe; AS drugoth, dryness, dry ground
base of drygo; see DRY] 1. dryness; absence of moisture, especially of
rain. 2. prolonged dry weather. 3. [Archaic] thirst. Also, drouth.

> Webster's New World Dictionary, College edition.

1. the condition or quality of being dry; dryness, aridity, lack of
   moisture (archaic).
2. dryness of weather or climate; lack of rain (current sense)
3. dry or parched land, desert (obsolete, rare)
4. thirst (archaic and dialect)
5. attributive and combined

> Oxford English Dictionary, Vol. III, D-E.

. . . a condition in which the amount of water that is needed for evapora-
tion and transpiration exceeds the amount actually available.

> Encyclopedia Britannica, VII (1963), 699.

Drought (Drouth) results from long-continued dry weather and lack or
insufficiency of rain which causes exhaustion of soil moisture, suffering of plants from lack of water, depletion of underground water supplies
and reduction and eventual cessation of stream flow."

> Ibid., p. 699.

Variations in Precipitation

. . . a spell of dry weather.

> Tannehill, Drought, Its Causes and Effects, preface.

a valley of rain deficiency in the broad sweep of time and weather.

> Ibid., p. 24.

(By international convention, the average precipitation over the 30-year
period [1921-1950] is referred to as the normal.)

Drought . . . a relatively temporary departure of the climate from the
normal or average climate toward aridity.

> Wayne C. Palmer, Weekly Weather and Crop Bulletin U. S. Weather
> Bureau, XLIV, No. 1a (January 10, 1957), 1.

European Russia
a period of ten days with a total rainfall not exceeding a fifth of an inch.

      Tannehill, Drought, Its Causes and Effects, p. 37.

U. S. Weather Bureau (one time)
. . . period of 30 days or more with deficient rainfall and not in excess of a fourth of an inch in any 24 hours.

      Ibid., p. 37.

England
an "absolute" drought . . . a period of 14 consecutive days without a hundredth of an inch on any one day.

      Ibid., p. 17.

a partial drought . . . a period of more than 28 days with rainfall averaging not more than one hundredth of an inch a day.

      Ibid., p. 37.

U. S. Weather Bureau, 1907 (approximately)
. . . a period of 21 days or more with rainfall 30 per cent or more below the normal.

      Ibid., p. 38

Arkansas 1933
. . . 15 days with no rain.

      Ibid., p. 38.

. . . in humid and semiarid state drought conditions exist when there is an annual deficiency of precipitation of 15 per cent or more.

      J. C. Hoyt, "Droughts of 1930-34," United States Geological Survey Water Supply Paper 680 (Washington: U. S. Government Printing Office, 1936), p. 2.

drought . . . a meteorological phenomenon which occurs during a period when precipitation is significantly less than the long-term average and when this deficiency is great enough and continues long enough to affect mankind.

      Thomas, p. 1.

drought was considered terminated by 0.10 inch or more of precipitation in 48 hours or less.

      George Blumenstock, Jr., "Drought in the United States Analyzed by Means of the Theory of Probability," United States Department of Agriculture Technical Bulletin B19 (Washington: U. S. Government Printing Office, 1942), p. 61.

drought . . . a prolonged and abnormal moisture deficiency."

      Palmer,"Meteorological Drought," p. 2

<u>Drought period</u> . . . an interval of time, generally of the order of month or years in duration, during which the actual moisture supply at a given place rather consistently falls short of the climatically expected or climatically appropriate moisture supply. Further, the severity of drought may be considered as being a function of both the duration and magnitude of the moisture deficiency.

<u>Ibid</u>., p. 3.

Effects on Vegetation

. . . a period of deficient rainfall that is seriously injurious to vegetation.

Tannehill, Drought, <u>Its Causes and Effects</u>, p. 39.

. . . drought conditions, as ordinarily defined in humid areas, exist when there is insufficient moisture in the soil to maintain plant life.

William G. Hoyt, "Droughts," <u>Hydrology</u>, ed. Oscar E. Meinzer (New York: Dover Publications, Inc., 1942), chap. xii, p. 579.

drought . . . refers to a specific period of time during which the total amount of rainfall recorded at a station is deficient to the extent that, more often than not, the corn yield falls below normal for the county in which the station is located."

Gerald L. Barger and H. C. S. Thom, "A Method for Characterizing Drought Intensity in Iowa," <u>Agronomy Journal</u>, XL (1949), 13-19.

drought . . . is considered to be a period when pasture growth is so far below normal that it affects adversely the animals grazing in particular areas.

S. L. Everist and G. R. Moule, "Studies in the Environment of Queensland. 2. The Climatic Factor in Drought," <u>The Queensland Journal of Agricultural Science</u>, Vol. IX, No. 3 (1952). Reprinted by the Queensland Department of Agriculture and Stock as Division of Plant Industry Bulletin No. 63 and Division of Animal Industry Bulletin No. 7.

. . . any period in which tree growth was reduced for five or more years has been considered to be a drought period.

Weakly, p. 2.

drought-day . . . a 24-hour period in which the soil moisture stress exceeds a limit, which, on the basis of experimental evidence, may be taken as a point at which the productive processes of the crop are being appreciably decreased.

C. H. M. Van Bavel, "A Drought Criterion and Its Application in Evaluating Drought Incidence and Hazard," <u>Agronomy Journal</u>, XLV (1953), 167-172.

A period of dry weather by or before the end of which vegetation is suffering from the lack of sufficient rainfall.

W. J. Humphreys, "How Droughts Occur," <u>Bulletin of the American Meteorological Society</u>, XII (1931), 18-22.

Economic and Social Effects

when precipitation is insufficient to meet the needs of established human
activities, drought conditions may be said to prevail.

> J. C. Hoyt, "Drought of 1936," United States Geological Water Supply
> Paper 820 (Washington: U. S. Government Printing Office, 1938), p. 2.

Drought defined in terms of (1) per cent departure from normal rainfall
(2) average crop and pasture conditions as a per cent of normal (3) per
cent increase or decrease in number of cattle (4) amount of Federal Aid
per capita.

> Kifer and Stewart.

. . . A droughty condition is created if, in the economic development
of a region, man creates a demand for more water than is normally available.

> William G. Hoyt, "Droughts," p. 580.

When acute moisture conditions occur two or more years in succession,
all economic activities are disrupted--the sêca (drought) has struck
once more.

> Hilgard O'Reilly Sternberg, "Geography's Contribution to the
> Better Use of Resources," The Future of the Arid Zone, ed.
> Gilbert F. White (Washington: American Association for the Ad-
> vancement of Science, 1956), pp. 200-220.

period when shortage of rainfall does cause distress to those who are
dependent on rain.

> Humphreys, p. 22.

Some Types of Drought

atmospheric drought . . . a period of strong wind, low precipitation,
high temperature, and unusually low relative humidity.

> Palmer, "Meteorological Drought," p. 2.

Agricultural drought . . . a condition of rainfall deficiency with respect to crop production.

> Barger and Thom, p. 519.

The chapman's drouth, that is the peddler's thirst, is proverbial in
Scotland because peddlers were accustomed to ask modestly for a glass
of water, when, in fact, they wanted food.

> Walter Scott, The Pirate, chap. VI (1821) as quoted in B. Steven-
> son (ed.), The MacMillan Book of Proverbs, Maxims, and Famous
> Phrases (New York: MacMillan, 1948).

permanent drought precipitation is never sufficient to meet the needs
expressed by the potential evapotranspiration.

> Thornthwaite, "Drought," p. 700.

contingent drought due to variations in precipitation from year to year.

Ibid.

seasonal drought due to an inadequate amount of precipitation in one season though other seasons may be adequate or even excessive in moisture amounts.

Ibid.

invisible drought a borderline inadequacy of rainfall, not quite enough to satisfy the crop needs from month to month, and which shows up only in reduced yields at the end of the year.

Ibid.

hydrologic drought . . . reductions in stream flow and in lake and reservoir levels, depletion of soil moisture, a lowering of the ground-water table, and consequent decrease in ground-water run off.

Palmer, "Meteorological Drought," p. 2.

APPENDIX II

QUESTIONNAIRE PERCEPTION OF DROUGHT HAZARD

I. General Information

1. How long have you been farming in this area? _____ years
   If all my life: How long has your family been in the area? _____ years
   If a newcomer: Where did you farm previously?

                                          similar area _____
                                          more humid area _____
                                          more arid area _____

2. How old are you? _____

3. Are you the owner, part owner, tenant or manager?

                                      owner _____
                                      part owner _____
                                      tenant _____
                                      manager _____
                                      other _____

4. How many dependents do you have? _____

5. How many years of school did you complete? _____ years

                        8th Grade or less _____
                        9-11 years _____
                        12 years--High School graduate _____
                        Technical Training _____
                        1-3 years college _____
                        College Grad (4 years) _____
                        Post Graduate _____
                        Not Applicable _____

6. What was your approximate gross farm income last year?

$50. -- 2,499	_____	$10,000 -- 19,999	_____
2500 -- 4,999	_____	20,000 -- 39,999	_____
5000 -- 9,999	_____	40,000 -- and over	_____

7. What is the exact nature of your operation?

                        straight grain _____
                  diversified (grain emphasis) _____
                  diversified (cattle interest) _____
                        other _____
                        specify other _____

   Have you ever changed in the past? Yes____ No ____ In what way? ____

8. Could you use the land in any other way? Yes ___ No ___
            If yes, How?   straight wheat _____
                                livestock _____
                                wheat and livestock _____
                                diversified crops _____
                                other _____

9. How much land do you have? Number of acres _____

10. Do you think you could stand poor crops better if you had a larger farm?

    Yes ___ No ___ Don't know ___ If yes: Why don't you get more land?

    None available ___ Cost too much ___ No funds ____

    Other _____

11. Have you increased the size of your farm in the past?   Yes___   No ___

II. Perception of Drought Hazard

12. What are the main advantages or disadvantages of this area?

Emphasizes advantages _____   Emphasizes disadvantages _____

Balanced treatment _____

Advantages: Disadvantages:

    Good soil _____   Too dry _____
    Level terrain _____   Too much hail _____
    Good climate _____   Insects _____
    Wide open spaces _____   Weeds _____
    Other _____   Floods _____
                                 Frost _____
                                 Isolation _____
                                 Other _____

13. Is there an effective water witcher in the area?

Strong belief _____   Belief _____   Neutral (undecided) _____

Doubt _____   Strong doubt _____

14. Would you consider the past few months to have been:

    Much wetter than usual _____   Wetter than usual _____
    Average _____   Drier than usual _____   Much drier than usual _____

15. How often do you expect a very good wheat crop?

    Every year ___   5 out of 10 ___   3 in 10 ___   1 in 10 ___
    1 in 4 ___   9 out of 10 ___   4 in 10 ___   2 in 10 ___   1 in 3 ___
    Other _____

What do you think of as a very good wheat crop? _____

How often do you need such a crop in order to keep going?
    Every year ____   1 year in 3 ____   Other ____
    Every Second year ____   1 in 4 ____

16. When was the last drought of this county? _____

17. Have you experienced any others? Yes ___   No ___
    If yes; what years? _____   What were they like? _____

18. Do you think a drought like the Dirty 30s will occur again?

    Definitely will _____
    Probably will _____
    Probably won't _____
    Will not _____
    Don't know _____

What do you think of as a drought?

    Rainfall _____   Crop yields _____
    Less than average _____   Lower than average _____
    Long dry spell (several months) _____   Much lower than average _____
    Several dry years _____   Crop failure (1 yr.) _____
    Other _____   Crop failure (several yrs.) __

19. What are the chances of drought next year?

    1 in 10 _____   3 in 10 _____   5 in 10 _____   2 in 10 _____

    4 in 1C _____   Less than 1 in 10 _____   Other _____

20. Suppose you had a drought this year. What would you expect next year? Would there be a greater or smaller risk of drought or would it make no difference?

        Greater _____   No difference _____

        Smaller _____   Don't know _____

21. Do you think droughts are becoming more or less frequent?

        More _____   No difference _____   Less _____   Don't know _____

22. If you were to live 100 years, how many drought years would you expect to have?

        100 _____   25 _____   10 _____   50 _____   20 _____

        5 _____   Other _____

III. Perception and Adoption of Applicable Practices

23. Is there any way to overcome droughts? Yes ___   No ___   Don't know ___

24. If a meeting were held and you were asked to give suggestions for reducing drought losses, what would you say?

Stubble mulch _____	Other tillage practices _____
Pump irrigation _____	Weather modification _____
Strip cropping _____	Summer fallow _____
Terracing _____	Adapted crops _____
Diversification _____	Insurance _____
Other _____	

25. What do you think of attempts at weather modification? Are they effective

        Strong belief _____   Doubt _____

        Belief _____   Strong doubt _____

            Maybe _____

26. Do you generally practice stubble mulch? Yes _____   No _____   What Year? ___

    If yes; why? Saves operations _____   Moisture control _____

    Erosion _____   Other _____

    If yes, does it seem to work? Yes _____   No _____

    If no, what are its disadvantages? Why don't you use it?

    Doesn't work here _____   Too dry, no stubble _____

    Too wet, stubble disappears _____   Need special machinery _____

    Not worth the extra effort _____   Prefer clean fields _____

    Other _____

27. Do you burn your stubble?

    Yes _____   No _____

28. How many times do you till the fields each year?

    As few as possible _____   6 or less _____

    Depends on the weather _____   7 to 10 _____

    After each rain _____   More than 10 _____

29. What sort of rotation do you follow? Continuous wheat _____

    Wheat fallow _____   Wheat, wheat, fallow _____

    Wheat, sorghum, fallow _____   Other _____

30. Do you vary this rotation at all? Yes ____   No ____

    If yes, when? According to soil moisture _____
                According to hunches _____
                With new methods _____
                Other _____

31. When do you usually seed your winter wheat? _____

    Does the planting date vary at all? Yes _____   No _____

    If yes, in what way? According to moisture _____
                  According to time available _____
                  Other _____

32. Do you use strip cropping (not contour farming)? Yes ____   No ____

    If yes, what is its main advantage? Erosion control _____
                      Moisture conservation _____
                      Other _____

    If no, is there any special reason why not?
    Doesn't work in this area _____   Adds to insect problem _____
    Too much extra work _____   No wind erosion here _____
    Other _____

33. Is your land suitable for terracing? Yes ___   No ___   Don't know ____

    Have you terraced your land? Yes ___   No ___   What year? _____
    If yes, what is the main value of it? Erosion control _____
    Moisture conservation _____   Other _____

    If no, is there any special reason why not?

        Too expensive _____   Doesn't do any good _____
        Too much extra work _____   Other _____

34. Is there much to be gained by fertilization of wheat here? Yes__   No __

    Do you fertilize your wheat? Yes ____   No ____
        If yes, what kind of fertilizer? When did you first use it?
        Nitrogen _____   Trace elements _____   Phosphorus _____   Other _____

        If no, why not? Too dry _____   Not worth expense _____
            No need (Soil good) _____   Doesn't do any good _____
            Other _____

35. What wheat varieties do you use? What year did you first use them?

Scout _____	Cheyenne _____	Nebred _____	Super Triumph _____
Lancer _____	Wichita _____	Bison _____	Kaw _____
Ottawa _____	Pawnee _____	Concho _____	Ponco _____
Warrior _____	Rodco _____	Triumph _____	Gage _____
Caddo _____	Turkey _____	Comanche _____	Other _____

    Do you ever plant more than one variety per year? Yes _____   No _____

36. Do you use irrigation? Yes____   No ____

    If yes, when did you start? _____

    If no, would you like to ? Yes ____   No ____
    What prevents you? Too expensive _____   No water ____
       Terrain unsuitable _____   Other _____

37. Some say luck plays an important part in success here and some say it
    doesn't. What do you think? Strong belief _____   Belief _____
    Maybe _____   Disbelief _____   Strong disbelief ____

38. How would you rate yourself as compared to your neighbors? Would you say that you are: Much luckier _____ Luckier _____ Equal _____ Unluckier _____ Much unluckier _____

39. Do you use crop insurance? Yes _____ No _____ Sometimes _____

    If yes, what kind? Hail _____ All crops _____ Other _____

    If sometimes, when do or don't you? Depends on:
       Weather _____ Crop _____ Hunches _____ Other _____

    If no, why don't you carry it? Too expensive _____
       Prefer self insurance _____ Other _____

40. Do you have sufficient reserves of grain and feed to carry you through a year of crop failure? Yes _____ No _____ Maybe _____

41. Do you have any off-farm income? Yes _____ No _____
       If yes, what? Part-time work _____ Investments _____
          Property _____ Other _____

42. In recent years did you borrow any money for seed, feed, fuel, etc. to get the crop in and harvested and carry your livestock? Yes ___ No ___

43. Are you more able to absorb a crop loss now than you were five years ago?

       Yes _____ No _____

44. How many years in a row could you hold out without serious problems?

       Indefinitely _____
       1 year _____ 3 years _____ 5 years _____
       2 years _____ 4 years _____ More than 5 years _____

45. Do you regularly keep written records on this farm?

       Yes _____ No _____ Sometimes _____

46. Which of the following best describes your way of operating?

    If a man plays it safe in the present, the future will take care of itself _____

    If a man takes chances when things look good, the future will take care of itself _____

    A man should be cautious, but able to take advantage of opportunities when they come up _____

    Too much long range planning makes a man too careful _____

    The man who plans ahead, is the man who will succeed _____

    It is good to plan ahead, but you also have to think about the big opportunities and have the courage to seize them _____

47. What are the main sources from which you obtain information about new practices in farming, such as about new machines, crop varieties, sprays, etc.?

       1. Farm magazines _____
       2. Neighbors or friends _____
       3. Family or relatives _____
       4. Co. Agent or Extension meetings _____
       5. Voc. Ag. Teacher--night school _____
       6. Extension or Experiment station bulletins _____
       7. Radio farm shows _____
       8. TV farm shows _____
       9. Newspapers _____
       10. State fair _____

11. County fair _____
12. Co-op. Extension Specialist _____
13. Experiment Station Staff _____
14. Staff training (Org.) _____
15. Other _____

    Which one is most important _____
    Which one is second most important _____

48. We know that all farm people don't adopt new practices at the same rate.

    About where would you rate yourself in respect to adopting new practices?

    Among the first _____   A little faster than most _____

    About average _____   A little slower than most _____

    Among the last _____   Don't know _____

IV. Interviewer Rating

Condition of Buildings:

    Excellent _____
    Fair _____
    Poor _____
    None _____

House Exterior and Surroundings:

    Flowers emphasized _____
    Lawns cared for _____
    Trees cared for _____
    Windbreak cared for _____
    House kept painted _____
    Picnic spot _____

Household decor:

    Old-fashioned, well kept _____
    Old-fashioned, poorly kept _____
    Mixed old and new, well kept _____
    Mixed old and new, poorly kept _____
    Relatively new middle class rural ____
    Relatively new above middle class ____
    Individual taste _____

Diversity: (town to farm):

    Wheat _____
    Cattle _____
    Corn _____
    Sorghum _____
    Other _____

APPENDIX III

RECORDS OF PAST DROUGHTS FOR INDIVIDUAL STUDY AREAS

TABLE 62

DROUGHTS HASTINGS, NEBRASKA, JANUARY, 1895-OCTOBER, 1964
(Number of Months of Drought at each Degree of Severity)

	Droughts		A. Extreme		B. Severe		Cum.
No.	1st Month	Last Month	Present	Cum. Total	Present	Cum. Total	Total A + B
1.	Dec. 1963	May 1964					
2.	Sept.1954	Feb. 1957	3	3	7	7	10
3.	June 1954	July 1954					
4.	Sept.1952	Oct. 1953					
5.	Apr. 1946	Aug. 1946					
6.	Oct. 1944	Mar. 1945					
7.	Nov. 1942	Dec. 1943			2	9	12
8.		May 1942					
9.	June 1933	Sept.1941	43	46	18	27	73
10.	Jan. 1931	Sept.1931					
11.	Feb. 1930	Mar. 1930					
12.	Mar. 1929	Aug. 1929					
13.	Nov. 1927	Sept.1928					
14.	Feb. 1926	Feb. 1927			4	31	77
15.	Nov. 1924	Aug. 1925					
16.	Feb. 1924	June 1924					
17.	June 1921	Mar. 1923			2	33	79
18.	Mar. 1918	Sept.1918					
19.	Aug. 1917						
20.	Sept.1916	Mar. 1917					
21.	Aug. 1913	Oct. 1913					
22.	Apr. 1911	June 1911					
23.	Apr. 1908						
24.	Mar. 1907						
25.	June 1906	Sept.1906					
26.	Apr. 1902						
27.	Dec. 1900	Aug. 1901					
28.	May 1900	June 1900					
29.	May 1899	Mar. 1900					
30.	Feb. 1896						

Total Number of Months, January, 1895-October, 1964 = 838

Per cent		5.5	3.9	9.4
Per cent 1924 base		9.3	6.3	15.7

TABLE 62--Continued

C. Moderate Present	Cum. Total	Cum. Total A+B+C	D. Mild Present	Cum. Total	Cum Total A+B+C+D	E. Incipient Present	Cum. Total	Cum. Total A-E	Total Present Drought
						5	5	5	5
9	9	19	4	4	23	5	10	33	28
			1	5	24	1	11	35	2
			5	10	29	6	17	46	11
			4	14	33	1	18	51	5
						2	20	53	2
2	11	23	5	19	42	3	23	65	12
						1	24	66	1
17	28	101	10	29	130	6	30	160	94
2	30	103	2	31	134	2	32	166	6
			1	32	135	1	33	168	2
1	31	104	3	35	139	2	35	174	6
2	33	106	3	38	144	4	39	183	9
6	39	116	1	39	155	2	41	196	13
			4	43	159	4	45	204	8
			2	45	161	2	47	208	4
8	47	126	9	54	180	1	48	228	20
2	49	128	2	56	184	2	50	234	6
						1	51	235	1
			2	58	186	4	55	241	6
			3	61	189	0	55	244	3
1	50	129	1	62	191	1	56	247	3
						1	57	248	1
						1	58	249	1
						2	60	251	2
						1	61	252	1
1	51	130	3	65	195	4	65	260	8
						2	67	262	2
			2	67	197	5	72	269	7
						1	73	270	1
	6.1	15.5		8.0	23.5		8.7	32.2	
	7.9	23.6		9.1	32.8		9.5	42.4	

TABLE 63

DROUGHTS MEDICINE LODGE, KANSAS, JANUARY, 1901-DECEMBER, 1964
(Number of Months of Drought at each Degree of Severity)

	Droughts		A. Extreme		B. Severe		Cum. Total A + B
No.	1st Month	Last Month	Present	Cum. Total	Present	Cum. Total	
1.	Jan. 1963	Oct. 1964			3	3	3
2.	Mar. 1962	May 1962					
3.	Apr. 1960	Jan. 1961					
4.	June 1952	Feb. 1957	23	23	20	23	46
5.	Oct. 1950	Jan. 1951					
6.	Apr. 1950	May 1950					
7.	Nov. 1945	Sept.1946			1	24	47
8.	Mar. 1943	Nov. 1943					
9.	Oct. 1938	Oct. 1940			6	30	53
10.	Oct. 1932	Mar. 1938	1	24	14	44	68
11.	July 1931	Oct. 1931					
12.	Feb. 1930	Feb. 1931					
13.	Feb. 1925	May 1927					
14.	Oct. 1922	Feb. 1923					
15.	Oct. 1921	Dec. 1921					
16.	Mar. 1921	May 1921					
17.	Aug. 1919	July 1920					
18.	Aug. 1916	Sept.1918			1	45	69
19.	Apr. 1914	Dec. 1914					
20.	Apr. 1913	Aug. 1913					
21.	Mar. 1910	Jan. 1911					
22.	Feb. 1909	Sept.1909					
23.	May 1906	June 1906					
24.	Nov. 1904	May 1905					
25.	Jan. 1904	Mar. 1904					
26.	Jan. 1903	Sept.1903					
27.	June 1901	Apr. 1902					

Total Number of Months, January, 1901-December, 1964 = 768

				Present		Present	A + B
Per Cent				3.1		5.8	9.0
Per Cent 1924 base				4.8		8.9	13.8

TABLE 63--Continued

C. Moderate		Cum. Total A+B+C	D. Mild		Cum. Total A+B+C+D	E. Incipient		Cum. Total A-E	Length of Present Drought
Present	Cum. Total		Present	Cum. Total		Present	Cum. Total		
15	15	18	3	3	21	1	1	22	22
			1	4	22	2	3	25	3
						7	10	32	7
3	18	64	8	12	76	3	13	89	57
			3	15	79	1	14	93	4
			2	17	81	0	14	95	2
2	20	67	4	21	88	3	17	105	10
5	25	72	3	24	96	1	18	114	9
8	33	86	2	26	112	3	21	133	19
28	61	129	12	38	167	5	26	193	60
			2	40	169	2	28	197	4
			11	51	180	2	30	210	13
3	64	132	12	63	195	6	36	231	21
			1	64	196	2	38	234	3
			2	66	198	1	39	237	3
			1	67	199	2	41	240	3
3	67	135	7	74	209	2	43	252	12
9	76	145	14	88	233	2	45	278	26
3	79	148	4	92	240	2	47	287	9
			1	93	241	4	51	292	5
3	82	151	5	98	249	3	54	303	11
			2	100	251	5	59	310	7
						2	61	312	2
			1	101	252	6	67	319	7
			1	102	253	2	69	322	3
			1	103	254	2	71	325	3
1	83	152	9	112	264	1	72	336	11
	10.7	19.7		14.6	34.4		9.4	43.8	
	13.0	26.8		12.8	39.6		7.3	46.9	

TABLE 64

DROUGHTS CURTIS, NEBRASKA, JANUARY, 1910-OCTOBER, 1964
(Number of Months of Drought at each Degree of Severity)

Droughts			A. Extreme		B. Severe		Cum. Total A + B
No.	1st Month	Last Month	Present	Cum. Total	Present	Cum. Total	
1.	May 1964	Oct. 1964					
2.	Aug. 1961						
3.	Sept.1960	Mar. 1961					
4.	July 1959						
5.	Feb. 1954	Mar. 1957	11	11	13	13	24
6.	June 1952	Sept.1953					
7.	Nov. 1950	Mar. 1951					
8.	Oct. 1949	Jan. 1950					
9.	Nov. 1945	Aug. 1946					
10.	Feb. 1943	Dec. 1943					
11.	Mar. 1936	Aug. 1941	8	19	12	25	44
12.	Sept.1932	Mar. 1935	6	25	5	30	55
13.	Oct. 1927	Apr. 1928					
14.	June 1925	Oct. 1926					
15.	Apr. 1924	July 1924					
16.	Feb. 1922	Apr. 1923			2	32	57
17.	Mar. 1920						
18.	Aug. 1919	Sept.1919					
19.	Mar. 1918	June 1918					
20	Mar. 1910	Apr. 1910					

Total Number of Months, January, 1910-October, 1964 = 658

Per Cent				3.8		4.9	8.7
Per Cent 1924 base				5.1		6.1	11.2

TABLE 64--Continued

C. Moderate		Cum. Total	D. Mild		Cum. Total	E. Incipient		Cum. Total	Total
Present	Cum. Total	A - C	Present	Cum. Total	A - D	Present	Cum. Total	A - E	Present Drought
			3	3	3	3	3	6	6
						1	4	7	1
						4	8	11	4
						1	9	12	1
11	11	35	2	5	40	1	10	50	38
2	13	37	7	12	49	4	14	63	13
			3	15	52	2	16	68	5
			2	17	54	2	18	72	4
3	16	40	4	21	61	3	21	82	10
2	18	42	6	27	69	3	24	93	11
21	39	83	9	36	119	6	30	149	56
2	41	96	12	48	144	4	34	178	29
			1	49	145	5	39	184	6
6	47	102	4	53	155	7	46	201	17
			2	55	157	1	47	204	3
9	56	113	1	56	169	2	49	218	14
						1	50	219	1
			1	57	170	1	51	221	2
			1	58	171	1	52	223	2
			1	59	172	1	53	225	2
	8.5	17.2		9.0	26.1		8.0	34.2	
	9.5	20.8		11.2	32.0		9.5	41.6	

TABLE 65

DROUGHTS GARDEN CITY, KANSAS, JANUARY, 1898-NOVEMBER, 1964
(Number of Months of Drought at each Degree of Severity)

Droughts			A. Extreme		B. Severe		Cum.
No.	1st Month	Last Month	Present	Cum. Total	Present	Cum. Total	Total A + B
1.	Aug. 1962	Nov. 1964	1	1	4	4	5
2.	Aug. 1960	Aug. 1961					
3.	Aug. 1955	Feb. 1957	6	7	3	7	14
4.	June 1952	Apr. 1955	2	9	4	11	20
5.	Nov. 1949	June 1950					
6.	Mar. 1945	Aug. 1946					
7.	Feb. 1943	Nov. 1943					
8.	Oct. 1940						
9.	Apr. 1934	Nov. 1939	24	33	31	42	75
10.	Sept.1931	July 1933			1	43	76
11.	Feb. 1930	Aug. 1930					
12.	Oct. 1926	Jan. 1928					
13.	Nov. 1924	Aug. 1925					
14.	Sept.1922	Mar. 1923					
15.	Nov. 1917	Aug. 1918					
16.	May 1916	Mar. 1917					
17.	Mar. 1914	Nov. 1914					
18.	Nov. 1912	Aug. 1913					
19.	Apr. 1911	Sept.1911					
20.	Sept.1910	Jan. 1911					
21.	Mar. 1910	June 1910					
22.	Mar. 1908	Oct. 1908					
23.	Oct. 1903	Apr. 1904					
24.	Aug. 1902	Sept.1902					
25.	Nov. 1901	Jan. 1902					
26.	June 1901	Aug. 1901					

Total Number of Months, January, 1898-November, 1964 = 803

Per Cent	4.1	5.4	9.5
Per Cent 1924 base	6.7	8.7	15.4

TABLE 65--Continued

C. Moderate		Cum. Total A+B+C	D. Mild		Cum. Total A+B+C+D	E. Incipient		Cum. Total A - E	Length Present Drought
Present	Cum. Total		Present	Cum. Total		Present	Cum. Total		
8	8	13	7	7	20	5	5	25	25
			1	8	21	9	14	35	10
1	9	23	7	15	38	2	16	54	19
23	32	52	5	20	72	0	16	88	34
2	34	54	4	24	78	2	18	96	8
3	37	57	4	28	85	8	26	111	15
1	38	58	3	31	89	4	30	119	8
						1	31	120	1
10	48	123	2	33	156	1	32	188	68
2	50	126	7	40	166	7	39	205	17
			3	43	169	4	43	212	7
3	53	129	6	49	178	4	47	225	13
2	55	131	2	51	182	3	50	232	7
1	56	132	5	56	188	1	51	239	7
						4	55	243	4
						6	61	249	6
			3	59	191	2	63	254	5
1	57	133	3	62	195	5	68	263	9
			2	64	197	4	72	269	6
			4	68	201	1	73	274	5
			3	71	204	1	74	278	4
			1	72	205	7	81	286	8
1	58	134	3	75	209	3	84	293	7
			2	77	211	0	84	295	2
						3	87	298	3
			2	79	213	1	88	301	3
	7.2	16.7	9.8	26.5			11.0	37.5	
	11.2	26.6	10.3	37.0			10.1	47.2	

TABLE 66

DROUGHTS KENTON, OKLAHOMA, JANUARY, 1901-DECEMBER, 1964
(Number of Months of Drought at each Degree of Severity)

	Drought		A. Extreme		B. Severe		Cum. Total A+B
No.	1st Month	Last Month	Present	Cum. Total	Present	Cum. Total	
1.	Apr. 1962	Dec. 1964			5	5	5
2.	May 1961						
3.	Apr. 1960	May 1960					
4.	Oct. 1958	Sept.1959					
5.	Sept.1951	Feb. 1957	6	6	34	39	45
6.	Oct. 1949	May 1950			1	40	46
7.	Oct. 1947	Nov. 1947					
8.	Apr. 1946	July 1946					
9.	Nov. 1945	Feb. 1946					
10.	Sept.1944	June 1945					
11.	May 1940	Oct. 1940					
12.	June 1939	Oct. 1939					
13.	July 1932	Aug. 1938	9	15	35	75	90
14.	July 1931	May 1932					
15.	Apr. 1930	Sept.1930					
16.	Aug. 1926	May 1927			1	76	91
17.	Aug. 1924	June 1925					
18.	Aug. 1922	Jan. 1923					
19.	Dec. 1921	Jan. 1922					
20.	May 1913	Aug. 1913					
21.	Nov. 1912	Dec. 1912					
22.	Mar. 1910	Sept.1911			1	77	92
23.	Feb. 1909						
24.	Sept.1907	Sept.1908					
25.	Apr. 1903	Aug. 1904			3	80	95
26.	Apr. 1902	Nov. 1902					

Total Number of Months January, 1901-December, 1964 = 768

Per Cent	2.0	10.4	12.4
Per Cent 1924 base	3.0	15.4	18.4

TABLE 66--Continued

| C. Moderate | | Cum. | D. Mild | | Cum. | E. Incipient | | Cum. | Length |
Present	Cum. Total	Total A+B+C	Present	Cum. Total	Total A+B+C+D	Present	Cum. Total	Total A - E	Present Drought
21	21	26	6	6	32	1	1	33	33
			1	7	33	0	1	34	1
			1	8	34	1	2	36	2
			1	9	35	5	7	42	6
14	35	80	2	11	91	8	15	106	64
2	37	83	4	15	98	1	16	114	8
			2	17	100	0	16	116	2
			1	18	101	1	17	118	2
						4	21	122	4
			2	20	103	4	25	128	6
3	40	86	2	22	108	1	26	134	6
			4	26	112	0	26	138	4
18	58	148	3	29	177	5	31	208	70
			1	30	178	4	35	213	5
			4	34	182	2	37	219	6
1	59	150	6	40	190	2	39	229	10
2	61	152	4	44	196	5	44	240	11
			4	48	200	2	46	246	6
						2	48	248	2
			1	49	201	3	51	252	4
						2	53	254	2
7	68	160	9	58	218	2	55	273	19
						1	56	274	1
2	70	162	1	59	221	5	61	282	8
4	74	169	7	66	235	2	63	298	16
			4	70	239	2	65	304	6
	9.6	22.0		9.1	31.1		8.5	39.6	
	12.3	30.8		8.9	39.8		8.9	48.7	

TABLE 67

DROUGHTS, EADS, COLORADO, JANUARY, 1924-NOVEMBER, 1964
(Number of Months of Drought at each Degree of Severity)

Droughts			A. Extreme		B. Severe		Cum. Total A + B
No.	1st Month	Last Month	Present	Cum. Total	Present	Cum. Total	
1.	Feb. 1963	Nov. 1964			5	5	5
2.	Aug. 1962	Oct. 1962					
3.	Sept.1958	July 1959					
4.	Aug. 1957	Feb. 1958					
5.	Mar. 1954	Mar. 1957	11	11	10	15	26
6.	May 1952	Sept.1953					
7.	Aug. 1951	Oct. 1951					
8.	Oct. 1950	May 1951					
9.	Sept.1949	June 1950			2	17	28
10.	Nov. 1945	July 1946					
11.	Aug. 1940	Feb. 1941					
12.	June 1939	Nov. 1939					
13.	Sept.1930	Oct. 1938	20	31	18	35	66
14.	Jan. 1930	Apr. 1930					
15.	Oct. 1927	Jan. 1928					
16.	Aug. 1926	May 1927					

Total Number of Months January, 1924-November, 1964 = 491

| Per Cent | | | 6.3 | | 7.1 | 13.4 | |

TABLE 67--Continued

C. Moderate		Cum. Total A+B+C	D. Mild		Cum. Total A+B+C+D	E. Incipient		Cum. Total A - E	Length Present Drought
Present	Cum. Total		Present	Cum. Total		Present	Cum. Total		
10	10	15	4	4	19	2	2	21	21
			2	6	21	1	3	24	3
						6	9	30	6
			1	7	22	6	15	37	7
3	13	39	9	16	55	4	19	74	37
13	26	52	3	19	71	1	20	91	17
						3	23	94	3
			1	20	72	7	30	102	8
2	28	56	4	24	80	1	31	111	9
			4	28	84	4	35	119	8
			2	30	86	4	39	125	6
1	29	57	4	34	91	1	40	131	6
23	52	118	12	46	164	11	51	215	84
1	53	119	2	48	167	1	52	219	4
			2	50	169	2	54	223	4
1	54	120	1	51	171	8	62	233	10
	11.0	24.4		10.4	34.8		12.6	47.2	

SELECTED BIBLIOGRAPHY

Drought and Climatology

Barger, G. L. "A Method of Characterizing Drought Intensity in Iowa,"
    Agronomy Journal, XLI (1949), 13-19.

Cronin, Francis D., and Beers, Howard W. Areas of Intense Drought Distress,
    1930-36. Works Progress Administration Research Bulletin, Series V,
    No. 1. Washington, January, 1937.

Dale, Robert F. "Changes in Moisture Stress Days Since 1933," Weather and
    Our Food Supply, CAED Report 20. Ames, Iowa: Center for Agricul-
    tural and Economic Development, 1964.

Federal Crop Insurance Corporation. Annual Report 1963. Washington: U.S.
    Department of Agriculture, April, 1964.

Fritts, Harold C. "Tree Ring Evidence for Climate Changes in Western North
    America," Monthly Weather Review, XCII, No. 7 (1965), 421-443.

Hare, F. K. "Climatic Classification," London Essays in Geography. Edited
    by L. D. Stamp and S.W.Woolridge. Cambridge: Harvard University
    Press, 1951. Chapter vii.

Mather, John. "The Role of Irrigation Agriculture in Humid Areas." Paper
    presented at the 61st Annual Meeting of the Association of American
    Geographers, Columbus, Ohio, April 18-21, 1965. Abstract in Annals
    of the Association of American Geographers, LV, No. 4 (1965), 631.

Palmer, Wayne C. "Meteorological Drought," U. S. Weather Bureau Research
    Paper No. 45. Washington: U. S. Department of Commerce, February,
    1965.

_____. "Climate Variability and Crop Production," Weather and Our Food
    Supply, CAED Report 20. Ames, Iowa: Center for Agricultural and
    Economic Development, 1964.

Penman, H. L. Vegetation and Hydrology. Technical Communication No. 53
    Commonwealth Bureau of Soils. Harpenden, Farnham Royal, Bucking-
    hamshire, England: Commonwealth Agricultural Bureau, 1963.

Rowe, William H. Federal Crop Insurance, A Description PA-408. Washing-
    ton: Federal Crop Insurance Corporation, October, 1959.

Russell, R. J. "Dry Climates of the United States, II, Frequency of Dry
    and Desert Years 1901-1920," University of California (Berkeley)
    Publications in Geography V, No. 5. Berkeley: University of
    California Press, 1932.

Sellers, William D. "Potential Evapotranspiration in Arid Regions," Journal of Applied Meteorology, III (1964), 96-104.

Tannehill, Ivan R. Drought; Its Causes and Effects. Princeton, N.J.: Princeton University Press, 1947.

_____. "Is Weather Subject to Cycles?" Water. The 1955 Yearbook of Agriculture. Washington: U. S. Government Printing Office, 1955.

Thomas, H. E. "General Summary of Effects of the Drought in the Southwest." Geological Survey Professional Paper 372-H. Washington: U. S. Government Printing Office, 1963.

Thornthwaite, C. W. "Drought," Encyclopedia Britannica, VII (1963), 699-701.

_____. "The Life History of Rainstorms: Progress from the Oklahoma Climatic Research Center," Geographical Review, XXVII (1937), 92-111.

_____. "Problems in the Classification of Climates," Geographical Review, XXXIII (1943), 233-255.

_____. "An Approach Toward A Rational Classification of Climate," Geographical Review, XXXVIII (1948), 55-94.

Thornthwaite, C. W., and Mather, J. R. "Instructions for Computing Potential Evapotranspiration and the Water Balance," Publications in Climatology, X, No. 3 (1957), 181-311.

Weakly, Harry E. "Recurrence of Drought in the Great Plains During the Last 700 Years," Northern Plains Branch, Soil and Water Conservation Research Division, Agricultural Research Service, USDA, in cooperation with Nebraska Agricultural Experiment Station, Lincoln, Nebraska. (Mimeographed.)

The Great Plains

General Background

Agricultural Research Service. "Farming in the Great Plains, A Survey of Financial and Tenure Situation in 1957," U. S. Department of Agriculture Production Research Report No. 50. Washington, D.C., 1961.

Alexander, Frank, and Kraenzel, Carl F. "Rural Social Organization of Sweet Grass County, Montana," Montana State College Agricultural Experiment Station Bulletin 490. Bozeman, November, 1953.

Bowden, Leonard W. Diffusion of the Decision to Irrigate, Simulation of the Spread of a New Resource Management Practice in the Colorado Northern High Plains. Chicago: University of Chicago, Department of Geography Research Paper No. 97, 1962.

Bowles, Gladys K. "An Analysis of Population Trends and Effects on Existing Institutions in the Great Plains," Proceedings of a State of Society Conference for Church Leaders, November 17-19, 1964. Edited by The Planning Committee Lincoln, Nebraska, Center for Continuing Education, 1965. Pp. 43-63.

Cleland, Courtney B. "Sutland and Yonland in North Dakota," North Dakota Institute for Regional Studies Social Science Report No. 1. Fargo: North Dakota Agricultural College, 1955.

Guest, Buddy Ross. Resource Use and Associated Problems in the Upper Cimarron Area. Chicago: University of Chicago, Department of Geography Research Paper No. 19, 1951.

Hecht, Melvin E. "Location Factors for Sidewalk Farmers in Elkhart, Morton County, Kansas." Unpublished Ph.D. dissertation, Department of Geography, University of Kansas, 1962.

Hewes, Leslie. "Wheat Failure in Western Nebraska 1931-1954," Annals of the Association of American Geographers, XLVII (1958), 375-397.

_____. "A Traverse Across Kit Carson County, Colorado, with Notes on Land Use on the Margin of the Old Dust Bowl, 1939-40 and 1962," Economic Geography, XXXIX (1963), 332-340.

_____. "Causes of Wheat Failure in the Dry Farming Region, Central Great Plains, 1939-1957," Economic Geography, XLI (1965), 313-330.

Hewes, Leslie, and Schmieding, Arthur C. "Geographical Patterns of Wheat Failure in Nebraska, 1931-1952," Geographical Review, XLVI (1956), 375-387.

Johnson, Vance. Heaven's Tableland. New York: Farrar, Straus, and Company, 1947.

Johnson, Willard D. "The High Plains and Their Utilization," United States Geological Survey, 21st Annual Report, Part IV (1899-1900), pp. 609-741.

_____. "The High Plains and Their Utilization," United States Geological Survey, 22nd Annual Report, Part IV (1900-1901, 1902), pp. 634-669.

Kifer, R. S., and Stewart, H. L. Farming Hazards in the Drought Area. Works Progress Administration Research, Monograph XVI. Washington, 1938.

Kollmorgen, Walter M. "Rainmakers on the Plains, Scientific Monthly, XL (1935), 146-162.

Kraenzel, Carl F. The Great Plains in Transition. Norman: University of Oklahoma Press, 1955.

_____. "The Rural Community and the Agricultural Program," Montana Agricultural Experiment Station Bulletin 552. Bozeman, June, 1960.

Krenz, Ronald D., and Miller, Thomas A. "Wheat Farming in Wyoming," University of Wyoming Agricultural Experiment Station Bulletins 391, 392 and 397. Laramie, 1962.

Lewis, G. M. "Changing Emphasis in the Description of the Natural Environment of the American Great Plains Area," Institute of British Geographers Publications, XXX (1962), 75-90.

Link, Irene. Relief and Rehabilitation in the Drought Area. Works Progress Administration Research Bulletin, Series V, No. 3. Washington, June, 1937.

173

Malin, James C. The Grassland of North America Prolegomena to Its History with Addenda. Lawrence, Kansas: By the author, 1961.

_____. "The Grassland of North America: Its Occupance and the Challenge of Continuous Reappraisals," Man's Role in Changing the Face of the Earth. Edited by William L. Thomas, Jr. Chicago: University of Chicago Press, 1956.

_____. Winter Wheat in the Golden Belt of Kansas. Lawrence: University of Kansas Press, 1944.

Powell, John W. Report on the Lands of the Arid Region of the United States. Washington: U. S. Government Printing Office, 1879.

Shantz, H. L. "The Natural Vegetation of the Great Plains Region," Annals of the Association of American Geographers, XIII (1923), 81-107.

Smith, Henry Nash. Virgin Land, The American West as Symbol and Myth. New York: Vintage Books, 1950.

Special Assistant to the President for Public Works Planning. Drouth A Report, A Report on Drouth in the Great Plains and the Southwest. Washington: U. S. Government Printing Office, October, 1958.

Taeuber, Conrad, and Taylor, Carl C. The People of the Drought States. Works Progress Administration Research Bulletin, Series V, No. 2. Washington, March, 1937.

Thornthwaite, C. Warren. "The Great Plains," Migration and Economic Opportunity, the Report of the Study of Population Redistribution. Edited by Carter Goodrich, Bushrod W. Allin, C. Warren Thornthwaite and others. Philadelphia: University of Pennsylvania Press, 1936.

U. S. Department of Agriculture. "Program for the Great Plains," U. S. Department of Agriculture Miscellaneous Publication No. 709. Washington, January, 1956.

U. S. Great Plains Committee. The Future of the Great Plains. Washington: U. S. Government Printing Office, 1936.

Webb, Walter Prescott. The Great Plains. New York: Grosset and Dunlap by arrangement with Ginn & Company, 1931.

Other Semi-Arid Areas

Barth, Fredrick. "Nomadism in the Mountain and Plateau Areas of South West Asia," UNESCO, The Problems of the Arid Zone, Proceedings of the Paris Symposium, Arid Zone Research Series XVIII. Paris: UNESCO, 1962.

Bowman, Isaiah. The Pioneer Fringe. New York: American Geographical Society, 1931.

Heathcote, R. L. "Conservation or Opportune Use? The Pastoralists' Problem in Semi-Arid Australia," Advancement of Science, XXI, No. 89 (1964), 47-60.

Jackson, W. A. Douglas. "The Virgin and Idle Lands of Western Siberia and Northern Kazakhstan: A Geographic Appraisal," Geographical Review, XLVI (1956), 492-508.

Jackson, W. A. Douglas. "The Virgin and Idle Lands Program Reappraised," Annals of the Association of American Geographers, LII, No. 1 (1962), 69-79.

Lewis, N. N. "The Frontier of Settlement in Syria: 1800-1950," International Affairs, XXXI (1955), 48-60.

Meinig, Donald W. On the Margins of the Good Earth, AAG Monograph Series. Chicago: Rand McNally & Company, 1962.

Mikesell, Marvin W. "Comparative Studies in Frontier History," Annals of Association of American Geographers, L (1960), 62-74.

Stamp, L. D. (ed.) A History of Land Use in Arid Regions, Arid Zone Research Series XVII. Paris: UNESCO, 1961.

Adaptation to Drought
Dry Farming Techniques and Management Strategies

Aanderud, Wallace A. "Income Variability of Alternative Plans, Selected Farm and Ranch Situations, Rolling Plains of Northwest Oklahoma." Unpublished Ph.D. dissertation, Department of Agricultural Economics, Oklahoma State University, 1964.

Bailey, Warren B. Organizing and Operating Dryland Farms in the Plains Environment. Summary of Regional Research Project GP-2.

Brangle, K. G., and Greb, B. W. "Comparison of Continuous Wheat and Wheat after Fallow in Colorado," Colorado State University Extension Service Bulletin 518-S. Fort Collins, December, 1963.

Castle, Emery N. "Adapting Western Kansas Farms to Uncertain Prices and Yields," Kansas State College Agricultural Experiment Station Technical Bulletin 75. Manhattan, February, 1954.

Chepil, W. A. "Width of Field Strips to Control Wind Erosion," Kansas State College Agricultural Experiment Station Technical Bulletin 92. Manhattan, December, 1957.

Drought Committee of the Nebraska College of Agriculture. "Adjusting to Drought, Choosing the Right Cropping Practices, University of Nebraska Extension Service Circular CC 151. Lincoln, March, 1957.

Erhart, Andrew B., Meger, Walter R., and Grover, Ben L. "Irrigation in Western Kansas," Kansas Agricultural Experiment Station Circular 324. Garden City, May, 1958.

Fenster, C. R. "Stubble Mulching with Various Types of Machinery," Soil Science Society of America Proceedings, XXIV, No. 6 (1960), 518-523. Reprinted as University of Nebraska College of Agriculture Extension Services Circular EC 61-134.

_____. "Stubble Mulch Judging," University of Nebraska Extension Service Circular EC 18-84-2.

_____. "Right Planting Dates = $," Nebraska Experimental Station Quarterly, Summer, 1963, Nebraska Agricultural Experimental Station Reprint QR 74.

Great Plains Research Technical Committee GP-2. Economic Problems in Great
    Plains Ranching, GP-2. Symposium. Bozeman, May 23-24, 1962.
    Bozeman: Great Plains Council Publication No. 22, October, 1964.

Hagerstrand, Torsten. "The Propagation of Innovation Waves," Readings in
    Cultural Geography. Edited by Marvin W. Mikesell and Philip L.
    Wagner. Chicago: University of Chicago Press, 1962. Originally
    published in Land Studies in Geography, Series B, Human Geography,
    Vol. IV (1952).

Hobbs, J. A., Luebs, R. E., and Bieberly, F. G. "Stubble Mulch Farming for
    Erosional Control," Kansas Agricultural Experiment Station Contribu-
    tion No. 644. Manhattan, December, 1960.

Jacobson, Paul, and Weiss, Walter. "Farming Terraced Land," U. S. Depart-
    ment of Agriculture Soil Conservation Service Leaflet No. 335.
    Washington: U. S. Government Printing Office, 1958.

Journal of Farm Economics, Vol. XXXII, No. 3 (1950).

Knight, Dale A. "Economic Considerations for Selecting the Superior Fre-
    quency of Fallow for Wheat in Three Locations in Western Kansas,"
    Kansas State College Agricultural Experiment Station Technical
    Bulletin 85. Manhattan, September, 1956.

Nelson, Aaron G. "Credit as a Tool for the Agricultural Producer," Great
    Plains Agricultural Council Publication No. 15. Lincoln:
    University of Nebraska College of Agriculture, 1957.

Rude, L. C. "Land Use Alternatives for Dryland Grain-Livestock Operators,"
    Montana Agricultural Experiment Station Bulletins 540, 571, 572.
    Bozeman, 1962.

Schaffner, L. W., Loftsgard, L. D., and Dahl, Norman. "Integrating Irriga-
    tion with Dryland Farming," North Dakota Agricultural Experiment
    Station Bulletin No. 433. Fargo, May, 1961.

Skrabanek, R. L., Banks, Vera J., and Bowles, Gladys K. "Farmer Adjustments
    to Drouth in a Texas County," Texas Agricultural Experiment Station
    Bulletin in B-1005 College Station: Texas A. & M. University,
    January, 1964.

Smika, D. E. "Fallow-Wheat-Sorghum: An Excellent Rotation for Dryland in
    Central Nebraska," Nebraska Agricultural Experiment Station Bulletin
    SB 483. Lincoln, June, 1964.

Stewart, T. G. "Keep Your Farm Productive by Controlled Summer Fallow,"
    Colorado State College Extension Service Circular 116-A. Fort
    Collins, April, 1937. Reprinted July, 1944.

Thair, Philip J. "Meeting the Impact of Crop Yield Risks in Great Plains
    Farming," North Dakota Agricultural Experimental Station Bulletin 392.
    Fargo, North Dakota, June, 1954.

Willsie, Roger H. "The Economics of Classifying Farmland between Alternative
    Uses," Nebraska Agricultural Experiment Station Research Bulletin
    208. Lincoln, March, 1963.

Zingg, A. W., and Whitfield, C. J. "A Summary of Research Experience with
    Stubble-Mulch Farming in Western United States," U. S. Department

of Agriculture Technical Bulletin No. 1166. Washington: U. S.
Government Printing Office, 1957.

Adaptation to Drought
Societal and Personality Adjustments

Bennett, John W. "Synopsis of a Cultural Ecology Research Program in
Saskatchewan," Plains Anthropologist, VIII, No. 20 (1963), 88.

Bennett, J. W., and Kohl, Seena. "Two Memoranda on Social Organization and
Adaptive Selection in a Northern Plains Region," Plains Anthropologist, VIII, No. 22 (1964), 10-22.

Botkin, B. A. (ed.) A Treasury of Western Folklore. New York: Crown
Publishers, 1951.

Crane, Stephen. "Waiting for the Spring," Prairie Schooner, XXXVIII, No. 1
(1964), 15-26.

Edwards, A. D. Influence of Drought and Depression on a Rural Community, A
Case Study in Haskell County, Kansas. The Farm Security Administra-
tion and the Bureau of Agricultural Economics cooperating, Social
Research Report No. VII. Washington, D.C., January, 1939.

Erikson E. Gordon. "Social and Cultural Features," Economic Development in
Southwestern Kansas, Part X. Lawrence: School of Business, Bureau
of Business Research, University of Kansas, March 1953.

Gordon, Ira J. "The Kansas Wheat Culture," Transactions Kansas Academy of
Science, LV (1952), 56.

Havens, A. Eugene. "A Review of Factors Related to Innovativeness," Ohio
Agricultural Experiment Station Mimeo Bulletin 329. Columbus: The
Ohio State University, February, 1962.

Kluckhohn, F. R., and Strodtbeck, F. L. Harvard University Project. "The
Comparative Study of Values in Five Cultures," Variations in Value
Orientations. Evanston : Row Peterson, 1961.

Photiadis, John D. "Contacts with Agricultural Agents," South Dakota Agricultural Experiment Station Bulletin 493. Brookings, 1960.

Peterson, Everett E. "Where the Coyotes Howl, and the Wind Blows Free,"
Proceedings of a State of Society Conference for Church Leaders
November 17-19, 1964, Lincoln, Nebraska. Lincoln: University of
Nebraska Press, 1965.

Rolvaag, O. E. Giants in the Earth. New York: Perennial Library, Harper
and Row, 1965.

Thomas, Franklin. The Environmental Basis of Society; A Study in the History
of Sociological Theory. New York and London, 1925; Reprint by
Johnson Reprint Corporation, 1965.

Tully, Joan, Wilkening, E. A., and Presser, H. A. "Factors in Decision
Making in Farming Problems," Human Relations, XVII, No. 4 (1964),
295-320.

Ullman, Edward. "Amenities as a Factor in Regional Growth," _Geographical Review_, XLIV, No. 1 (1954), 119-132.

Vogt, Evon S., and Hyman, Roy. _Water Witching U.S.A._ Chicago: University of Chicago Press, 1959.

Whitmore, Bruce G. "Developing Potential Human and Physical Resources in the Plains Area." Unpublished Master's dissertation, Department of Education, Colorado State University, 1961.

Personality Theory and Projective Techniques

Beck, Robert J. "A Comparative Study of Spatial Meaning." Unpublished Master's thesis, Committee on Human Development, University of Chicago, 1964.

Henry, William E. "The Business Executive: The Psychodynamics of a Social Role," _The American Journal of Sociology_, LIV, No. 4 (1949), 286-291.

_____. "Executive Personality and Job Success," _Personnel Series No. 120_. New York: American Management Association, 1948.

_____. _The Analysis of Fantasy The Thematic Apperception Technique in the Study of Personality_. New York: John Wiley and Sons, Inc., 1956.

Lindzey, Gardner. _Projective Techniques and Cross-Cultural Research._ New York: Appleton-Century-Crofts, 1961.

McClelland, David C. _The Achievement Motive_. New York: Appleton-Century-Crofts, 1953.

_____. "The Achievement Motive in Economic Growth." Paper delivered at North American Conference on the Social Implications of Industrialization and Technological Change, Chicago, 1960.

_____. _The Achieving Society_. Princeton, N.J.: Van Nostrand, 1961.

Murray, Henry A. _Explorations in Personality_. New York: Science Editions, 1962. Originally published by Oxford University Press in 1930.

_____. _Thematic Apperception Test: Pictures and Manual_. Cambridge: Harvard University Press, 1943.

Schaw, Louis C., and Henry, William E. "A Method of the Comparison of Groups: A Study in Thematic Apperception," _Genetic Psychology Monographs_, LIV (1956), 207-253.

Sims, John N. "Psychodynamics of Two Levels of Executives in Federal Civil Service." Unpublished Ph.D. dissertation, Committee on Human Development, University of Chicago, 1964.

Spaulding, Irving A. "Farm Operator Time-Space Orientations and the Adoption of Recommended Practices," _Rhode Island Agricultural Station Bulletin_ 330. Kingston: University of Rhode Island, June, 1955.

Symonds, P. M. "Criteria for the Selection of Pictures for Investigation of Adolescent Fantasies," _Journal of Abnormal and Social Psychology_, XXXIV (1939), 271-274.

Choice of Area--Basic References

Hammond, Edwin H. "Analysis of Properties in Land Form Geography: An Application to Broad-Scale Land Form Mapping," Annals of the Association of American Geographers, LIV, No. 1 (1964), 11-19.

_____. "Classes of Land-Surface Form in the Forty-Eight States," Map Supplement No. 4. Washington, D.C.: Association of American Geographers, 1963.

Kiowa County Agricultural Advisory Council. "Farm and Ranch Guide for Kiowa County," Colorado State Agricultural Extension Service Handbook. Fort Collins: Colorado State University Extension Service, August, 1958.

Küchler, A. W. Potential Natural Vegetation of the Coterminous United States. Special Publication No. 36. New York: American Geographical Society, 1964.

U. S. Department of Agriculture. (Map.) "Major Land Uses in the United States." Washington: U. S. Department of Agriculture, Bureau of Agricultural Economics, 1950.

Van Royen, William. The Agricultural Resources of the World. Vol. I Atlas of the World's Resources. New York: Prentice-Hall, 1954. Fig. 36, p. 32.

Perception and Man-Milieu Hypotheses
Theoretical Statements

Ackerman, E. "Where Is a Research Frontier?" Annals of the Association of American Geographers, LIII (1963), 429-440.

Barrows, Harlan H. "Geography as Human Ecology," Annals of the Association of American Geographers, XIII (1923), 1-14.

Chein, Isidor. "The Environment as a Determinant of Behavior," The Journal of Social Psychology, XXXIX (1954), 115-127.

Darby, H. C. "The Problem of Geographical Description," Transactions and Papers The Institute of British Geographers, No. 30 (1962), pp. 1-13.

Dennis, Wayne. "Cultural and Developmental Factors in Perception," Perception an Approach to Personality. Edited by Robert R. Blake and Glenn V. Ramsey. New York: The Ronald Press, 1951.

Firey, Walter. Man Mind and Land: A Theory of Resource Use. Glencoe, Illinois: Free Press, 1960.

Glacken, Clarence J. "Changing Ideas of the Habitable World," Man's Role in Changing the Face of the Earth. Edited by W. L. Thomas, Jr. Chicago: University of Chicago Press, 1956.

Kirk, William. "Problems of Geography," Geography, XLVII, Part 4 (1963), 357-371.

Kirk, William. "Historical Geography and the Concept of the Behavioral Environment," Indian Geographical Journal: Silver Jubilee Edition 1951. Madras: Indian Geographical Society, 1952.

Lowenthal, David. "Geography, Experience and Imagination: Towards a Geographical Epistemology," Annals of the Association of American Geographers, LI, No. 3 (1961), 241-260.

MacLeod, R. B. "The Phenomenological Approach to Social Psychology," Psychological Review, LIV (1947), 193-210.

Mary Annette, Sister. "Social Geography: Methodological Considerations." Paper presented at 61st Annual Meeting of Association of American Geographers, at Columbus, Ohio, April 21, 1965.

Marsh, George Perkins. Man and Nature, or, Physical Geography as Modified by Human Action. New York: Scribner, Armstrong and Company, 1864.

Rostlund, Erhard. "Twentieth Century Magic," Readings in Cultural Geography. Edited by Marvin W. Mikesell and Philip L. Wagner. Chicago and London: University of Chicago Press, 1962.

Semple, Ellen C. Influences of the Geographic Environment. New York: Henry Holt and Company, 1911.

Sonnenfeld, J. "Environmental Perception and Adaptation Level in the Arctic." Paper presented at the 61st Annual Meeting of Association of American Geographers, at Columbus, Ohio, April 20,1965.

Sorre, Max. Géographie Psychologique. Traité de Psychologie Appliquée, Livre VI, Conditions et regles de Vie. Paris: Presses Universitaires de France, 1955.

Spoehr, Alexander. "Cultural Differences in the Interpretation of Natural Resources," Man's Role in Changing the Face of the Earth. Edited by W. L. Thomas, Jr. Chicago: University of Chicago Press, 1956.

Sprout, Harold and Margaret. Man-Milieu Relationship Hypotheses in Context of International Politics. Princeton, New Jersey: Princeton University Center of International Studies, 1956.

_____. The Ecological Perspective on Human Affairs with Special Reference to International Politics. Princeton, New Jersey: Princeton University Press, 1965.

Stoddart, D. R. "Geography and the Ecological Approach; The Ecosystem as a Geographic Principle and Method," Geography, L, Part 3 (1965), 242-251.

Thomas, William L., Jr. (ed.) Man's Role in Changing the Face of the Earth. Chicago: University of Chicago Press, 1956.

Tuan, Yi Fu. "The Problem of Geographic Description." Paper presented at the 60th Annual Meeting of the Association of American Geographers, Syracuse, New York, March 29-April 1, 1964.

_____. "Attitudes Toward Environment: Themes and Approaches." Paper presented at 61st Annual Meeting of Association of American Geographers at Columbus, Ohio, April 20, 1965.

Tuan, Yi Fu. "Topophilia or Sudden Encounter with the Landscape," Landscape, XI (Autumn, 1961), 29-32.

UNESCO. Environmental Physiology and Psychology in Arid Conditions: Proceedings of the Lucknow Symposium. Arid Zone Research Series,
XXIV. Paris: UNESCO, 1964).

UNESCO. Environmental Physiology and Psychology in Arid Conditions, Reviews
of Research. Paris: UNESCO, 1963.

White, Gilbert. "The Choice of Use in Resource Management," Natural Resources
Journal, I (1961), 23-40.

Whittlesey, D. "Horizon of Geography," Annals of the Association of
American Geographers, XXXV (1945), 1-36.

Some Perceptual and Man-Milieu Studies in Other Fields

Psychology

Allport, Floyd H. Theories of Perception and the Concept of Structure.
New York: Wiley, 1955.

Bareleson, B., and Steiner, G. Human Behavior An Inventory of Scientific
Findings. New York: Harcourt, Brace and World, 1964.

Bevan, William. "Perception: Evolution of a Concept," Psychological Review,
LXV, No. 1 (1958), 34-55.

Klein, George S. "The Personal World Through Perception," Perception
an Approach to Personality. Edited by R. R. Blake and Glenn V.
Ramsey. New York: The Ronald Press, 1951.

Psychoanalysis

Eriksen, E. Childhood and Society. New York: W. W. Norton & Co., 1950.

_____. "Ego Development and Historical Change," Psychoanalytic Study of
the Child, II, 359-395.

Fromm, E. Escape from Freedom. New York: Farrar and Rinehart, 1941.

Horney, K. The Neurotic Personality of Our Time. New York: W. W. Norton
and Co., 1953.

Kardiner, A. Psychological Frontiers of Society. New York: Columbia
University Press, 1945.

_____. The Individual and His Society. New York: Columbia University
Press, 1939.

Munroe, Ruth L. Schools of Psychoanalytic Thought. New York: The Dryden
Press, 1955.

Sullivan, H. S. The Interpersonal Theory of Psychiatry. New York: W. W.
Norton and Co., 1953.

Developmental Psychology

Hunt, J. McVickers. Intelligence and Experience. New York: Ronald Press, 1961.

Kessen and Kuhlman. "Symposium on Thought in Young Children." Monograph for Society of Research in Child Development, Vol. XXVII, No. 2 (1962).

Piaget, Jean. The Child's Conception of the World. Patterson, New Jersey: Littlefield, Adams and Co., 1960.

Anthropology

Conklin, Harold C. "An Ethnoecological Approach to Shifting Agriculture," Readings in Cultural Geography. Edited by Philip L. Wagner and Marvin W. Mikesell. Chicago: University of Chicago Press, 1962.

_____. Hanunoo Agriculture. F. A. O. Forestry Development Paper No. 12. Rome, FAO of United Nations, 1957.

D'Andrade, Roy Goodwin, and Romney, A. Kimball (ed.) "Transcultural Studies in Cognition," American Anthropologist, Vol. LXVI, No. 3, Part 2 (1964).

Frake, Charles O. "Cultural Ecology and Ethnography," American Anthropologist, LXIV, No. 1 (1962), 53-59.

_____. "Transcultural Studies in Cognition," American Anthropologist, LVI, No. 3, Part 2 (1964).

Kluckhohn, C., and Murray, N. A. (eds.) "Personality Formation: The Determinants," Personality in Nature, Society and Culture. New York: Knopf, 1953.

Lindesmith, A. R., and Strauss, A. L. "A Critique of Culture--Personality Writhings," American Sociological Review, XV (1950), 587-600.

Malinowski, Bronislaw. The Coral Gardens and Their Magic. 2 vols. New York: American Book Co., 1935.

Whorf, Benjamin Lee. "Science and Linguistics," Readings in Social Psychology. Edited by Maccoby et al. New York: Holt, Rinehart, and Winston, Inc., 1958.

Social Psychology

Asch, S. E. "Effects of Group Pressure upon the Modification and Distortion of Judgments," Readings in Social Psychology. Edited by Maccoby et al. New York: Holt, Rinehart, and Winston, Inc., 1958.

Bruner, Jerome S. "Social Psychology and Perception," Readings in Social Psychology. Edited by Maccoby et al. New York: Holt, Rinehart, and Winston, Inc., 1958.

Klineberg, Otto. Tensions Affecting International Understanding A Survey of Research. Social Science Research Council Bulletin 60. New York, 1950.

McClelland, D. C., and Atkinson, J. W. "The Projective Expression of Needs: I. The Effect of Different Intensities of Hunger Drive on Perception," Journal of Psychology, XXV (1948), 205-222.

Postman, L., and Bruner, J. S., and McGinnies, E. "Personal Values as Selective Factors in Perception," Journal of Abnormal and Social Psychology, XXCIII (1948), 148-153.

Sherif, M. The Psychology of Social Norms. New York: Harper and Brothers, 1963.

Perception: Empirical Studies

Appleyard, Donald, Lynch, Kevin, and Myer, John. The View from the Road. Cambridge, M.I.T. Press, 1964.

Blaut, J. et al. "A Study of Cultural Determinants of Soil Erosion and Conservation in the Blue Mountains of Jamaica," Social and Economic Studies, VIII (1959), 402-420.

Burton, Ian. Types of Agricultural Occupance of Flood Plains in the U.S. Chicago: University of Chicago, Department of Geography Research Paper No. 75, 1962.

_____. "Invasion and Escape on the Little Calumet," Papers on Flood Problems. Edited by G. F. White. Chicago: University of Chicago, Department of Geography Research Paper No. 70, 1960.

Burton, Ian, and Kates, Robert W. "The Floodplain and the Seashore," Geographical Review, LIV (1964), 366-385.

Burton, Ian, Kates, Robert W., Mather, John R., and Snead, Rodman E. The Shores of Megalopolis: Coastal Occupance and Human Adjustment to Flood Hazard. Publications in Climatology, XVIII, No. 3 (1965), 435-603. Elmer, New Jersey: C. W. Thornthwaite Associates Laboratory of Climatology.

Fonaroff, L. Schuyler. "Conservation and Stock Reduction on the Navaho Tribal Range," Geographical Review, LIII (1963), 200-223.

Gould, Peter R. "Man Against His Environment: A Game Theoretic Framework," Annals of the Association of American Geographers, LIII (1963), 290-297.

Haddon, John. "A View of Foreign Lands," Geography, LXV (1960), 286-289.

Heathcote, R. L. "Historical Changes in the Appraisal of Pastoral Land Resources," Review of Marketing and Agricultural Economics, XXXI (1963), 3-23.

Hill, A. David. The Changing Landscape of a Mexican Municipio Villa Las Rosas, Chiapas. Chicago: University of Chicago, Department of Geography Research Paper No. 91, 1964.

Kates, Robert W. Hazard and Choice Perception in Flood Plain Management. Chicago: University of Chicago, Department of Geography Research Paper No. 78, 1962.

Kates, Robert W., and Wohlwill, Joachim F. "The Impact of the Non-Social

Environment." Unpublished manuscript regarding a proposed number of Journal of Social Issues.

Lowenthal, David. "Not Every Prospect Pleases," Landscape, Winter 1962, pp. 19-23.

Lowenthal, David, and Prince, Hugh C. "The English Landscape," Geographical Review, LIV, No. 3 (1964), 309-346.

_____. "English Landscape Tastes," Geographical Review, LV, No. 2 (1965), 186-222.

Lucas, Robert. "Wilderness Perception and Use: The Example of the Boundary Waters Canoe Area," Natural Resources Journal, III, No. 3 (1963), 394-411.

Lynch, Kevin. The Image of the City. Cambridge, Massachusetts: Technology Press and Harvard University Press, 1960.

Mitsuhashi, Setsuko. "Geographic Concepts of High School Students." Unpublished Master's thesis, Department of Geography, University of Chicago, 1962.

Natural Resources Journal, Vol. III, No. 3 (1964). Contains symposium on Perception and Natural Resources.

Porter, Philip W. "Suk Views on Suk Environments." Paper read at the meetings of the American Association of Geographers, Denver, Colorado, September 1-5, 1963.

_____. "Pokot Ideas Concerning Soil." A chapter on Pokot. (Mimeographed.)

_____. "Environmental Potentials and Economic Opportunities: A Background for Cultural Adaptation," American Anthropologist, LXVII, No. 2 (1965), 409-420.

Roder, Wolf. "Attitude and Knowledge on the Topeka Flood Plain," Papers on Flood Problems. Edited by G. F. White. Chicago: University of Chicago, Department of Geography Research Paper No. 70.

Rogers, Everett M. Diffusion of Innovations. New York: The Free Press of Glencoe, 1962.

Vogt, Evon S. Modern Homesteaders, The Life of a Twentieth Century Frontier Community. Cambridge: The Belknap Press of Harvard University Press, 1955.

White, Gilbert F. Choice of Adjustment to Floods. Chicago: University of Chicago, Department of Geography Research Paper No. 93, 1964.

White, Gilbert F. et al. Changes in the Urban Occupance of Flood Plains in the United States. Chicago: University of Chicago, Department of Geography Research Paper No. 57.

White, Gilbert F. Human Adjustment to Floods. Chicago: University of Chicago, Department of Geography Research Paper No. 29, 1945.

Wolpert, Julian. "The Decision Process in Spatial Context," Annals of the Association of American Geographers, LIV (1964), 537-558.

THE UNIVERSITY OF CHICAGO
DEPARTMENT OF GEOGRAPHY
RESEARCH PAPERS (Lithographed, 6 × 9 Inches)

(Available from Department of Geography, Rosenwald Hall, The University of Chicago, Chicago, Illinois, 60637. Price: four dollars each; by series subscription, three dollars each.)

*1. GROSS, HERBERT HENRY. *Educational Land Use in the River Forest–Oak Park Community (Illinois)*

*2. EISEN, EDNA E. *Educational Land Use in Lake County, Ohio*

*3. WEIGEND, GUIDO GUSTAV. *The Cultural Pattern of South Tyrol (Italy)*

*4. NELSON, HOWARD JOSEPH, *The Livelihood Structure of Des Moines, Iowa*

*5. MATTHEWS, JAMES SWINTON. *Expressions of Urbanism in the Sequent Occupance of Northeastern Ohio*

*6. GINSBURG, NORTON SYDNEY. *Japanese Prewar Trade and Shipping in the Oriental Triangle*

*7. KEMLER, JOHN H. *The Struggle for Wolfram in the Iberian Peninsula, June, 1942—June, 1944: A Study in Political and Economic Geography in Wartime*

*8. PHILBRICK, ALLEN K. *The Geography of Education in the Winnetka and Bridgeport Communities of Metropolitan Chicago*

*9. BRADLEY, VIRGINIA. *Functional Patterns in the Guadalupe Counties of the Edwards Plateau*

*10. HARRIS, CHAUNCY D., and FELLMANN, JEROME DONALD. *A Union List of Geographical Serials*

*11. DE MEIRLEIR, MARCEL J. *Manufactural Occupance in the West Central Area of Chicago*

*12. FELLMANN, JEROME DONALD. *Truck Transportation Patterns of Chicago*

*13. HOTCHKISS, WESLEY AKIN. *Areal Pattern of Religious Institutions in Cincinnati*

*14. HARPER, ROBERT ALEXANDER. *Recreational Occupance of the Moraine Lake Region of Northeastern Illinois and Southeastern Wisconsin*

*15. WHEELER, JESSE HARRISON, JR. *Land Use in Greenbrier County, West Virginia*

*16. MCGAUGH, MAURICE EDRON. *The Settlement of the Saginaw Basin*

*17. WATTERSON, ARTHUR WELDON. *Economy and Land Use Patterns of McLean County, Illinois*

*18. HORBALY, WILLIAM. *Agricultural Conditions in Czechoslovakia, 1950*

*19. GUEST, BUDDY ROSS. *Resource Use and Associated Problems in the Upper Cimarron Area*

*20. SORENSEN, CLARENCE WOODROW. *The Internal Structure of the Springfield, Illinois, Urbanized Area*

*21. MUNGER, EDWIN S. *Relational Patterns of Kampala, Uganda*

*22. KHALAF, JASSIM M. *The Water Resources of the Lower Colorado River Basin*

*23. GULICK, LUTHER H. *Rural Occupance in Utuado and Jayuya Municipios, Puerto Rico*

*24. TAAFFE, EDWARD JAMES. *The Air Passenger Hinterland of Chicago*

*25. KRAUSE, ANNEMARIE ELISABETH. *Mennonite Settlement in the Paraguayan Chaco*

*26. HAMMING, EDWARD. *The Port of Milwaukee*

*27. CRAMER, ROBERT ELI. *Manufacturing Structure of the Cicero District, Metropolitan Chicago*

*28. PIERSON, WILLIAM H. *The Geography of the Bellingham Lowland, Washington*

*29. WHITE, GILBERT F. *Human Adjustment to Floods: A Geographical Approach to the Flood Problem in the United States*

30. OSBORN, DAVID G. *Geographical Features of the Automation of Industry*   1953. 120 pp.

*31. THOMAN, RICHARD S. *The Changing Occupance Pattern of the Tri-State Area, Missouri, Kansas, and Oklahoma*

*32. ERICKSEN, SHELDON D. *Occupance in the Upper Deschutes Basin, Oregon*

*33. KENYON, JAMES B. *The Industrialization of the Skokie Area*

*34. PHILLIPS, PAUL GROUNDS. *The Hashemite Kingdom of Jordan: Prolegomena to a Technical Assistance Program*

*35. CARMIN, ROBERT LEIGHTON. *Anápolis, Brazil: Regional Capital of an Agricultural Frontier*

36. GOLD, ROBERT N. *Manufacturing Structure and Pattern of the South Bend–Mishawaka Area* 1954. 224 pp. 6 folded inserts. 2 maps in pocket.

*37. SISCO, PAUL HARDEMAN. *The Retail Function of Memphis*

*38. VAN DONGEN, IRENE S. *The British East African Transport Complex*

*39. FRIEDMANN, JOHN R. P. *The Spatial Structure of Economic Development in the Tennessee Valley*

*40. GROTEWOLD, ANDREAS. *Regional Changes in Corn Production in the United States from 1909 to 1949*

*41. BJORKLUND, E. M. *Focus on Adelaide—Functional Organization of the Adelaide Region, Australia*

*42. FORD, ROBERT N. *A Resource Use Analysis and Evaluation of the Everglades Agricultural Area*

*43. CHRISTENSEN, DAVID E. *Rural Occupance in Transition: Sumter and Lee Counties, Georgia*

*44. GUZMÁN, LOUIS E. *Farming and Farmlands in Panama*

* Out of print.

*45. ZADROZNY, MITCHELL G. *Water Utilization in the Middle Mississippi Valley*

*46. AHMED, G. MUNIR. *Manufacturing Structure and Pattern of Waukegan–North Chicago*

47. RANDALL, DARRELL. *Factors of Economic Development and the Okovango Delta*
1956. 282 pp. (Research Paper No. 3, Program of Education and Research in Planning, The University of Chicago.)

48. BOXER, BARUCH. *Israeli Shipping and Foreign Trade* 1957. 176 pp.

49. MAYER, HAROLD M. *The Port of Chicago and the St. Lawrence Seaway* 1957. 283 pp.

*50. PATTISON, WILLIAM D. *Beginnings of the American Rectangular Land Survey System, 1784–1800*

*51. BROWN, ROBERT HAROLD. *Political Areal-Functional Organization: With Special Reference to St. Cloud, Minnesota*

*52. BEYER, JACQUELYN. *Integration of Grazing and Crop Agriculture: Resources Management Problems in the Uncompahgre Valley Irrigation Project*

53. ACKERMAN, EDWARD A. *Geography as a Fundamental Research Discipline* 1958. 40 pp. $1.00.

*54. AL-KHASHAB, WAFIQ HUSSAIN. *The Water Budget of the Tigris and Euphrates Basin*

*55. LARIMORE, ANN EVANS. *The Alien Town: Patterns of Settlement in Busoga, Uganda*

56. MURPHY, FRANCIS C. *Regulating Flood-Plain Development* 1958. 216 pp.

*57. WHITE, GILBERT F., et al. *Changes in Urban Occupance of Flood Plains in the United States*

*58. COLBY, MARY MC RAE. *The Geographic Structure of Southeastern North Carolina*

*59. MEGEE, MARY CATHERINE. *Monterrey, Mexico: Internal Patterns and External Relations*

60. WEBER, DICKINSON. *A Comparison of Two Oil City Business Centers (Odessa-Midland, Texas)*
1958. 256 pp.

61. PLATT, ROBERT S. *Field Study in American Geography* 1959. 408 pp.

62. GINSBURG, NORTON, editor. *Essays on Geography and Economic Development* 1960. 196 pp.

63. HARRIS, CHAUNCY D., and FELLMANN, JEROME D. *International List of Geographical Serials*
1960. 247 pp.

*64. TAAFFE, ROBERT N. *Rail Transportation and the Economic Development of Soviet Central Asia*

*65. SHEAFFER, JOHN R. *Flood Proofing: An Element in a Flood Damage Reduction Program*

66. RODGERS, ALLAN L. *The Industrial Geography of the Port of Genova* 1960. 150 pp.

67. KENYON, JAMES B. *Industrial Localization and Metropolitan Growth: The Paterson-Passaic District* 1960. 250 pp.

68. GINSBURG, NORTON. *An Atlas of Economic Development*
1961. 119 pp. 14 × 8½". Cloth $7.50. University of Chicago Press.

69. CHURCH, MARTHA. *Spatial Organization of Electric Power Territories in Massachusetts*
1960. 200 pp.

70. WHITE, GILBERT F., et al. *Papers on Flood Problems* 1961. 234 pp.

71. GILBERT, E. W. *The University Town in England and West Germany*
1961. 79 pp. 4 plates. 30 maps and diagrams.

72. BOXER, BARUCH. *Ocean Shipping in the Evolution of Hong Kong* 1961. 108 pp.

73. ROBINSON, IRA M. *New Industrial Towns on Canada's Resource Frontier*
1962. (Research Paper No. 4, Program of Education and Research in Planning, The University of Chicago.) 192 pp.

74. TROTTER, JOHN E. *State Park System in Illinois* 1962. 152 pp.

75. BURTON, IAN. *Types of Agricultural Occupance of Flood Plains in the United States*
1962. 167 pp.

76. PRED, ALLAN. *The External Relations of Cities During 'Industrial Revolution'* 1962. 124 pp.

77. BARROWS, HARLAN H. *Lectures on the Historical Geography of the United States as Given in 1933*
Edited by WILLIAM A. KOELSCH. 1962. 248 pp.

78. KATES, ROBERT WILLIAM. *Hazard and Choice Perception in Flood Plain Management*
1962. 157 pp.

79. HUDSON, JAMES. *Irrigation Water Use in the Utah Valley, Utah* 1962. 249 pp.

80. ZELINSKY, WILBUR. *A Bibliographic Guide to Population Geography* 1962. 257 pp.

*81. DRAINE, EDWIN H. *Import Traffic of Chicago and Its Hinterland*

*82. KOLARS, JOHN F. *Tradition, Season, and Change in a Turkish Village*

83. WIKKRAMATILEKE, RUDOLPH. *Southeast Ceylon: Trends and Problems in Agricultural Settlement*
1963. 163 pp.

84. KANSKY, K. J. *Structure of Transportation Networks: Relationships between Network Geometry and Regional Characteristics* 1963. 155 pp.

85. BERRY, BRIAN J. L. *Commercial Structure and Commercial Blight* 1963. 254 pp.

86. BERRY, BRIAN J. L., and TENNANT, ROBERT J. *Chicago Commercial Reference Handbook*
1963. 278 pp.

87. BERRY, BRIAN J. L., and HANKINS, THOMAS D. *A Bibliographic Guide to the Economic Regions of the United States* 1963. 128 pp.

88. MARCUS, MELVIN G. *Climate-Glacier Studies in the Juneau Ice Field Region, Alaska* 1964. 128 pp.

89. SMOLE, WILLIAM J. *Owner-Cultivatorship in Middle Chile* 1964. 176 pp.

90. HELVIG, MAGNE. *Chicago's External Truck Movements: Spatial Interaction between the Chicago Area and Its Hinterland* 1964. 132 pp.

* Out of print.

91. HILL, A. DAVID. *The Changing Landscape of a Mexican Municipio, Villa Las Rosas, Chiapas*
   NAS-NRC Foreign Field Research Program Report No. 26. 1964. 121 pp.
92. SIMMONS, JAMES W. *The Changing Pattern of Retail Location*   1964. 212 pp.
93. WHITE, GILBERT F. *Choice of Adjustment to Floods*   1964. 164 pp.
94. MCMANIS, DOUGLAS R. *The Initial Evaluation and Utilization of the Illinois Prairies, 1815–1840*
   1964. 109 pp.
95. PERLE, EUGENE D. *The Demand for Transportation: Regional and Commodity Studies in the United States*   1964. 130 pp.
96. HARRIS, CHAUNCY D. *Annotated World List of Selected Current Geographical Serials in English*   1964. 32 pp. $1.00
97. BOWDEN, LEONARD W. *Diffusion of the Decision To Irrigate: Simulation of the Spread of a New Resource Management Practice in the Colorado Northern High Plains*   1965. 146 pp.
98. KATES, ROBERT W. *Industrial Flood Losses: Damage Estimation in the Lehigh Valley*
   1965. 76 pp.
99. RODER, WOLF. *The Sabi Valley Irrigation Projects*   1965. 213 pp.
100. SEWELL, W. R. DERRICK. *Water Management and Floods in the Fraser River Basin*   1965. 163 pp.
101. RAY, D. MICHAEL. *Market Potential and Economic Shadow: A Quantitative Analysis of Industrial Location in Southern Ontario*   1965. 164 pp.
102. AHMAD, QAZI. *Indian Cities: Characteristics and Correlates*   1965. 184 pp.
103. BARNUM, H. GARDINER. *Market Centers and Hinterlands in Baden-Württemberg*   1966. 126 pp.
   NAS-NRC Foreign Field Research Report No. 27. 1966. 173 pp.
104. SIMMONS, JAMES W. *Toronto's Changing Retail Complex*   1966. 126 pp.
105. SEWELL, W. R. DERRICK, *et al. Human Dimensions of Weather Modification*   1966. 423 pp.
106. SAARINEN, THOMAS FREDERICK. *Perception of the Drought Hazard on the Great Plains.*   1966. 198 pp.